THE CREDIT CRUNCH DIARIES

The financial crisis by those who made it happen

Best Wishes

Nick.

David Lascelles and Nick Carn

Edited by Jay Elwes

Illustrations by Joe Cummings

CSFI

CENTRE FOR THE STUDY
OF FINANCIAL INNOVATION

ISBN-13: 978-0-9561904-5-1

Designed and typeset by Karen Tuzee
tuzee@cybersmart.co.za

Printed and bound
by Heron, Dawson, Sawyer

About the authors

David Lascelles, former banking editor of the *Financial Times*, is now senior fellow at the Centre for the Study of Financial Innovation.

Nick Carn is a partner at Odey Asset Management.

Contents

CHAPTER FOUR

CHAPTER FIVE

Introduction

A rnold Parquet, senior compliance officer, and Edward Gershon, CEO of the fictional entity Amalgamated Finance for Europe (AFFE) made their debut in the pages of *Financial World* in Feb 2006.

The original idea was that the bickering between them would provide a light-hearted commentary on the everyday business of banking. What we didn't know at the time was that banking was about to emerge from the shadows. Shrieking horribly, it did rather more than merely emerge – it proceeded to run stark naked through the streets to the consternation and disgust of the population at large.

The collapse of Northern Rock, the first run on a British bank since before World War One, still lay in the future. So did the collapse of Bear Stearns, Lehman Brothers and AIG. Hank Paulson, the US Treasury secretary and ex-Goldman Sachs banker, had not yet fallen on his knees before the Democrat speaker of the House, Nancy Pelosi, to beg her for support for his bank rescue plan. ("I didn't know you were a Catholic, Hank," she said.) The phrase "credit crunch" was not yet in general usage and the crash in the world's property and stock markets was yet to come. Bernie *"Made-off"* Madoff's

$50bn fraud was still undetected and his associate Ezra Merkin was still Chairman of GMAC. Iceland was still best known for its geysers and Robert Peston and Fred Goodwin had yet to win their special places in the hearts of the British nation. It would have been hard to have made any of it up.

Against the backdrop of such a lurid reality, the fictional world of AFFE necessarily appears monochrome. By real world standards the behaviour of the AFFE workforce is very restrained. Their love lives are confined to wistful longings for their co-workers while apparently nobody in the bank exhibits psychopathic tendencies or believes in alien abduction, astrology or magic crystals. This is not, of course, intended to be believable.

Done from life, however, is the sense of carrying on as before, irrespective of the storms raging outside. In spite of hearing non-stop about the financial crisis, no one at AFFE expects to lose their job until they are called into their supervisor's office. Bridget Brace, the faultlessly PC head of Human Resources, diligently updates her seminal (sic) tome *Respect at Work*, unperturbed by the ever-dwindling number of AFFE employees available either to respect or disrespect one another. In the same way, Tony Imbroglio, self-styled (or so Gershon maintains) head of security would be astonished at the suggestion that his job was threatened by strange impersonal forces.

Finally, there's nothing funny about people losing their jobs or about the human cost of the credit crunch, but as the events of the last 18 months have shown, life is frequently both tragic and absurd at the same time.

David Lascelles and Nick Carn

The Credit Crunch timeline

Feb 2006

Widespread discontent at Amalgamated Finance for Europe (AFFE) over bonuses. All departments and individuals feel they have been unfairly discriminated against.

Nov 2006

Bridget Brace, head of Human Resources completes *Respect at Work 2007*, setting out the central objectives for AFFE's human resource policy in the year ahead.

Apr 2007

New Century Financial, US specialist subprime lender, files for Chapter 11 bankruptcy.

July 2007

Bear Stearns closes two credit hedge funds. Investors face a total loss.

Sep 2007

Run on Northern Rock. Fed cuts main rate to 4.75%.

Oct 2007

Citigroup announces subprime losses of $5.9bn. Bridget puts finishing touches to *Respect at Work 2008*.

Jan 2008

World stock markets have biggest fall since dotcom collapse.

Feb 2008

Northern Rock is nationalised.

Mar 2008

Bear Stearns in shotgun marriage to JP Morgan. AFFE's Gershon secures an injection of new capital from a Far East sponsor.

May 2008

UBS announces $37bn in losses related to US mortgages.

July 2008

AFFE's Parquet behaves shamefully on a trip to Moscow where he has been despatched to do due diligence on potential merger partner Sibgazbank.

Sep 2008

Lehman Brothers files for bankruptcy. Parastatal mortgage giants Fannie Mae and Freddie Mac are taken into "conservatorship".

Nov 2008

IMF aid to Ukraine and Iceland.

Dec 2008

Bernard Madoff is arrested,
charged with a $50bn fraud.
Parquet performs an amusing
song at the AFFE Christmas
party. FTSE stock market
index closes down 31.3%
on the year, the DAX 40.4%
and the CAC 42.7%.

Jan 2009

President elect Barack Obama
describes America's economy
as "very sick". AFFE's deputy
compliance officer commences "carrotplan" diet.

Feb 2009

Bank of England cuts rates to 1%.

Mar 2009

AIG announces a quarterly loss of $61.7bn. UK Treasury apparatchik
James Grimm installed at AFFE.

June 2009

General Motors follows Chrysler into bankruptcy.

July 2009

Goldman Sachs announces record profits. *Rolling Stone* magazine
describes it as a "Giant Poison Squid".

THE CREDIT CRUNCH DIARIES

The financial crisis
by those who made it happen

1

The Ancien Regime

Before anyone had heard of the Credit Crunch there was a world in which everyone lived in harmony. The economies grazed peacefully under the watchful eyes of the Central Bankers. Alan Greenspan called it the "Great Moderation" and it seemed that each economic cycle would be less severe than the last.

The dotcom and technology boom had collapsed, but the economy had hardly missed a beat. Some worried that economic stability had been bought at the expense of ever more debt; others argued that greater job security meant that it was safe to borrow more. In those days many people didn't know what a Collateralised Mortgage Obligation was, even though they might not have been able to buy their house if one hadn't been invented. Either way, the people were happy; they worked, they played, they fell in love and they bought houses. Lots of houses.

If the truth be told, not everyone was completely happy. Some people envied bankers because of their large bonuses. And the bankers? They envied other bankers whose bonuses were bigger then theirs. One of the places where not everyone was *completely* happy was AFFE. And the reason? Bonuses.

A New Year's resolution

Parquet blogs:

Tues 3 Jan 2006: A New Year and a new resolution: I've decided to keep a private blog. It's got to be private because as a Senior Compliance Officer at Amalgamated Finance for Europe, I know too much about what goes on in this firm. But I need an outlet for my feelings. Even Compliance Officers have souls.

My worry right now is bonuses. Business is good, deals are pouring in, despite soaring oil prices. We might even make record profits for 2005. Staff expectations are high. I've noted that on the trading floor they're already putting in orders for new Porsches. Putting the cart before the horse, as it were!!

Of course, Compliance Officers don't get bonuses. Management only measures profit as money earned, not money saved. When I think of the thousands, (millions!) that Risk Controls – enforced by this department – have spared the firm in losses, it makes me wonder where justice lies. Compliance Officers get their reward in heaven.

But that's not the point. It's not healthy. Bonuses are skewing the business. I've seen all those cut-price flotations, those "collateralised mortgage obligations" that no one understands, least of all the German *Landesbanks* who get stuffed with them. Those cosy deals with hedge funds. Most of that business should never have been done. Let's have some healthy incentives, a decent share-out of well-earned profits. Nothing wrong with that.

The rumour is that bonuses are going to be 100% of salary. I must talk to someone on the executive floor about this.

Must also finish reading the FSA's new paper on the EU's new blockbuster Markets in Financial Instruments Directive (MiFID). This is obviously required reading. I'll need to prepare a briefing for the board.

Thurs 5 Jan: Saw Gershon, the CEO, this morning. He gave me precisely 30 seconds. "Bonuses are not a compliance matter," he said. I said: "They are if it encourages people to take crazy risks". "That's what you're there for," he replied, waving me out of the room.

This afternoon they were all trooping in to get their packages. Whoop-pees echoed round the building. It will be all over the papers tomorrow, even the *FT*. "City fat cats coin £ms!!" No wonder people hate us.

Fri 6 Jan: I knew it. The combination of bonus pay-outs and 24-hour pub licenses was lethal. Binge drinking doesn't even begin to describe it. Broadgate this morning is littered with AFFE bodies, and at least three people are facing charges of drunk and disorderly.

Gershon was steaming through the hall, yelling at everyone. When I passed, he looked at me as if it was my fault. I just shrugged, and went to my cubicle and got on with drafting my MiFID briefing paper.

Later. The magistrates were obviously infected by festive spirit: they bound the three over to keep the peace – first offences. I happen to know that these guys are incorrigible. Sent a message to that effect to Will Barrow, the head trader (whose bonus, incidentally, was over half a million). He was not amused. "Just keep out of this," he messaged back. I replied that, as Senior Compliance Officer, I could do what I liked, and he'd just better keep his team in order.

Went home for the week-end feeling I'd made my point. Must try and finish that MiFID paper.

Mon 9 Jan: Was puzzled this morning to receive a parcel marked for my personal attention, delivered by courier. It turned out to be a case of Bulgarian red. There was a message: "An admirer". We have a strict company rule on gifts, specially in the Compliance Department. I must call up our community outreach people and get it put in a raffle.

Had another bad session with Gershon late in the day. He wants me (why me?) to issue a circular to staff about behaviour in public places. He was in a dinner jacket as he spoke, preparing to go out to a dinner, chauffeur-driven limo at the door. I left the building in such a huff that I forgot to take the MiFID file to read on the train.

Tues 10 Jan: Was on the phone to the FSA this morning about the MiFID paper when an email from Gershon flashed up on the screen: "Come over at once!" Cradling the phone on my shoulder I typed back: "Can't. I'm talking to FSA…"

About two seconds later he stormed into my cubicle. "You do what I say," he said. I tried to keep calm, but I could see he was spoiling for a fight. His eye caught the case of plonk. I'd forgotten to give it away. "What's this? An admirer!" He burst out laughing. "Pathetic! Parquet, you just damn well better get your act together or you're out. Gifts however small will not be tolerated in this department."

As he whirled out, I caught sight of Barrow sniggering at the far end of the room. Bastard!

Parquet

Gershon blogs:

Tues 3 Jan 2006: I was at a dinner at my old college at Cambridge last night and was sitting next to an historian, not unattractive in a slightly left wing sort of way. She was talking about using archive material and how helpful diaries are to historians and how the main actors in any age have a responsibility to future generations to leave a proper record. I strongly suspect that the entire conversation had a lot to do with fundraising for some ghastly new graduate centre, but the upshot was that she persuaded me to keep a diary. "Main actors". I must say, it does have a pleasing ring.

The bank has had an exceptional year. One of the most important parts of my job is to ensure that staff, particularly senior staff, are properly incentivised. Unfortunately, whatever one does, someone will feel hard done by.

Thurs 5 Jan: The delicate business of deciding bonus allocations is interrupted by the appearance of Arnold Parquet. He is a new man recently hired to beef up our compliance function. I must confess that my first impressions have been quite unfavourable. While I know that one should not be over influenced by appearance, he radiates a sort of physical intrusiveness which could easily become vexatious upon long exposure. Never mind. He reports jointly to John Sutton our CFO so I don't expect much day-to-day contact and, after all, one doesn't need to be best friends to have a fruitful working relationship. I am quite taken aback, however, when it transpires that he seems to think that compensation policy is part of his remit. Politely but firmly I wave him away. I must have a word with John.

Fri 6 Jan: Lots of unfavourable publicity in today's newspapers of the "Fat Cat Banker" variety. Really, haven't these people got anything better to do? Even more tiresome is the fact that we have a disciplinary problem. Some of the "lads" went on the town last night and are facing charges of being drunk and disorderly. Happily the magistrate had rather more sense than they do and they were sent home.

Will Barrow, our head mortgage-backed trader, calls me to say that the wretched Parquet has stuck his nose into this as well. The man's only been here a matter of weeks and he's already put everyone's back up. I call John to get him to deal with it, only to find he's talking at some kind of accountancy rally. Rather him than me.

Mon 9 Jan: I'm all dressed up and just about to leave the office when Parquet comes up to me in the lift lobby and starts to bleat about "behaviour in public places" as he primly puts it. I tell him that if he feels so strongly about it he should circulate a memo. Good grief, what's the matter with him?

Tues 10 Jan: I'm supposed to be running an international bank but it seems that most of my time is to be spent dealing with Parquet. Apparently he's been accepting gifts without reporting them (quick work, I must say, given how long he's been with us). I email him to come to my office straight away. He emails back that he's busy. I go straight round to his desk – he really does have some learning to do. What should greet my eyes but the offending article itself – a box of some execrable Bulgarian plonk. I really had to laugh.
Gershon

The consumer boom and the escalating levels of personal debt are already starting to attract attention by the spring of 2006. The Federal Reserve Bank would raise interest rates to 5.25% in June bringing to an end the very low rates which had been available on adjustable rate mortgages. Delinquencies on "subprime" mortgages, as loans to poorer quality borrowers were known, would rise to a record in September. The term "Ninja loans": no income, no job, and no assets, was to come later. Specialist mortgage lenders played their role in the boom, but so did a number of Government initiatives intended to end the supposed practice of refusing to lend in some districts, then known as "zip code apartheid".

Aside from rising concern about consumer debt, one of the concurrent real world stories was that of the so called "NatWest Three", who were accused of ripping off their employer NatWest Bank in a transaction involving the purchase of a special purpose vehicle set up for the now defunct Enron. Actually business left over from the last cycle, many of the themes – fraud, complex accounting and financial innovation among them – struck contemporary chords. New extradition procedures, established as part of the "war on terror", were invoked to get the three to stand trial in the United States, although the alleged crime had taken place in the UK. Much press outrage was expended on the iniquity of the new legislation, emphasising that the accused would have been treated differently in the UK. They were duly extradited, tried, found, as Gershon suggested, "guilty as weasels in a henhouse" and sent to prison. Some felt that those outraged about the new arrangements had found an unfortunate cause to champion.

~

Personal lending

Parquet blogs:

Mon 24 Apr: The press is having another go at the banks today over the latest consumer debt figures. The Brits are the most indebted people in Europe, over £3,000 for every man, woman and child. "Usurers!" was the headline in the *Sun*. *The Guardian* had a leader calling for a windfall tax on bank lending. "Bring irresponsible banks to heel," it said. Well did you ever! Treating banks like dogs! I bet whoever wrote that leader has a huge mortgage and buys everything on credit. People just don't connect.

Tues 25 Apr: I was thinking overnight about consumer debt, and decided to review AFFE's position. After all, if there's going to be a political row, we need to be on top of the issues, ready to fight off attacks. Also, AFFE must have a strong loan book in case the Bank of England decides to push interest rates up again.

As soon as I got into the office I called up Paul Scheme who runs our personal lending business and asked him how it was going. "Everything's fine," he said. "We've got it all under control." I pressed him: "But what if the government cracks down?" Scheme replied: "They wouldn't dare. Millions of people live off credit."

I've been in the Compliance Business more than 20 years, and I know that when people talk like that, it means trouble. They're trying to fob me off, to deny reality. I must find out more. This could be tricky. I'll have to postpone my report on MiFID for the board. They'll be disappointed.

Wed 26 Apr: I called up Finance and asked for the latest numbers on personal lending. I have to say I was amazed. Our mortgages have gone up 25 per cent this year, and unsecured loans even more. Bad debts are also rising. This is far worse than I realised, and it could mean trouble.

I rang up Scheme again and pointed this out. "What if the housing market crashes?" I asked. "Run along, Parquet," he said. Run along! You can't say that to a Senior Compliance Officer! His reaction has really convinced me that we're in deep trouble.

In my job, it's my difficult but stern responsibility to bring uncomfortable facts to the notice of senior management. I shall prepare a memo for Gershon saying that AFFE is exposing itself to financial and political risk with its personal lending strategy. I shall say that while this business brings in short-term profits, it's storing up trouble for the future. It's courting regulatory crackdown and public hostility, damaging our reputation. And so on.

Thurs 27 Apr: I was working on my memo when Gershon called me over. He was having a senior management meeting to discuss the final quarter figures. Paul Scheme was there too, and he gave me a superior look.

Gershon seemed pleased. The year-end figures will be good. Revenues and profits are well up and ahead of analysts' forecasts. He's going to propose another dividend hike to the board. And there'll be big bonuses. I was very relieved to hear all this, specially in light of my worries about excesses in personal lending.

But then came a bombshell. Gershon turned round to Scheme and said: "I particularly want to single out the contribution from personal lending. Profits up by more than 50 per cent, and strong growth on all fronts. Well done Paul!"

Gershon led a round of applause. Fortunately I was holding a stack of files and couldn't free my hands. Scheme beamed: "And we're about to launch a really good credit card promotion," he said. "Free transfers, zero charge and a special low interest rate! We should pull in half a million new customers." Gershon added: "That's my man!"

As we filed out, Scheme patted me on the shoulder in a patronising way. "Like I told you, Parquet," he said. "It's all going great."

Fri 28 Apr: I spent a terrible night. I knew that AFFE's good results were a myth, built on a dodgy personal lending book and a credit card promotion that was just giving money away to flaky borrowers. But what was I to do?

My duty was clear. I had to complete my memo and send it over to Gershon. He was on the phone immediately. "Come over," he said. I walked into his office, trembling. He had my memo in his hands.

"This is a good piece of work, Parquet," he said. "And I know you're right. But if you think you've got a tough job, mine's even tougher. There are times when you have to drive the business forward and take the risks. I can't put the brakes on growth just because we're worried about things that may never happen. Here, have a cigar, and I'll recommend you for a bonus."

I didn't know whether to laugh or cry.

Parquet

Gershon blogs:

Mon 24 Apr: A thoroughly indifferent start to the week. Looking at the newspapers in the car on the way to work I'm unable to avert my eyes in time to avoid the unedifying spectacle of the fifth estate eagerly wielding the sword of justice. Two stories stir its righteous ire. Apparently banks are responsible for the growth of consumer credit. Next week's exposé – greengrocers responsible for growth of carrot sales.

Not content with this scoop they have decided to champion the cause of some hapless, US-bound extraditees who are clearly as guilty as weasels in a henhouse. Why is it that whenever the US does anything there are howls of execration, but whenever the European Court of Justice embarks on one of its frequent campaigns to expand its pernicious influence the effort is either ignored or applauded?

Tues 25 Apr: This man Parquet is really becoming a nuisance. He's now sticking his nose into our personal lending business. Why can't he just get on with his job of ticking the right boxes and sending the correct forms off to the ever growing army of regulators? Some progress on the MiFID report would also be welcome.

Wed 26 Apr: Monthly meeting with John our CFO. Apart from the usual drivel about "resources" and his apparently chronic inability to hire anyone who can do their job properly there's a whole lot of stuff about a "new regulatory environment", the upshot of which appears to be that the wretched Parquet is now the most important person in the bank and he is to be humoured, flattered, promised his own fig tree and the attentions of fifty doe-eyed virgins in the afterlife etc at each and every available opportunity. I explain to John that an important aspect of his role in this "new environment" will be to ensure that my interaction with Parquet is absolutely minimal.

Thurs 27 Apr: Quarterly management meeting to go over the figures. Parquet shows up to provide compliance oversight (lord help us). Sales ahead of budget in all our business lines. Personal lending particularly strong. Well done Paul Scheme. Parquet sits looking vaguely discontented. Still no sign of the MiFID report, of course.

Fri 28 Apr: A report arrives from Parquet. Is it the MiFID report? No, it is not the MiFID report. It is a report in which he says that the bank's lending policies are knowingly and deliberately reckless. I call him into my office, as usual he seems strangely disconnected from events. We really don't need him whining to the regulators and generally stirring it up, so I make some generally conciliatory noises, important member of team, shared objectives, discretionary senior management bonus pool and so on. He just gawps at me. He really is a most peculiar man.

Gershon

~

Widening the deposit base

Parquet blogs:

Mon 21 Aug: Brussels is a dirty word in the City. No doubt about that. Everyone links it with massive rule books and annoying intrusion. Why can't we run the City ourselves? It's been amazingly successful without the help of Brussels.

I used to think all that. But I've just spent a camping holiday on the Continent (we have a Firestorm camper with gas fire and shower which I can strongly recommend), and I've come back with different ideas. Having the euro was incredibly useful as we travelled from one country to another. In the old days we had to have travellers cheques, and we lost money every time we cashed them into local currency. Not any more. I'm beginning to think that "Europe" might not be such a bad idea after all.

Trouble is that Gershon can't stand anything to do with the EU. All he can think of is officious eurocrats telling him what to do. His attitude makes it incredibly difficult to implement the new EU regulations in the bank, and there are enough of them. My back-to-work resolution is to turn the tide of opinion in AFFE and make everyone love Europe. But how?

Tues 22 Aug: I've decided to write a paper showing how the EU's Financial Services Action Plan can be of incredible benefit to an international institution like AFFE. It will open up new markets and really put us at the cutting edge of international finance. I think that Kitty Ussher, the new City minister, is absolutely right when she says we have to be "at the top table, talking", rather than just sulking outside. Also, I gather that Charlie McCreevy, the EU commissioner in charge of the single market, is "on our side" when it comes to breaking down barriers.

As luck would have it, Gershon is due to go to Paris on Thursday to talk to the French about expanding our branch to take on retail customers. Just the opportunity to show him how we can take advantage of EU rules to enlarge our business. I'm sure he'll come round.

Wed 23 Aug: I hope I'm right about Gershon. When I took my paper to him this morning I found him reading a brief from one of the eurosceptic organisations urging him to oppose the new EU constitutional treaty. "Bad for the City, bad for everyone", it was called. I made a joke about "EU-phoria", but he didn't seem to get it.

I really hope he takes my message on board. At the end of the day, we don't have a choice. If we don't go along with Brussels, what's the alternative? We'd be all on our own.

Thurs 24 Aug: Spent the day rather nervously awaiting the outcome of Gershon's visit.

Decided to catch up on the press. Was greatly comforted by an article in *Financial World* interviewing the chairman of the London Investment Bankers' Association. He was very pro-EU, saying that Brussels "is striving to create a businesslike and competitive environment", and that measures like MiFID will "break down the parochial monopolies".

There was also a piece in the *Financial Times* saying that EU regulation is so good that everyone else is copying it. I have to agree. Much better than the Americans who have totally shot themselves in the foot with Sarbanes-Oxley. Ended the day feeling most encouraged. Once you get to grips with all this stuff and cut through eurosceptic propaganda, it really looks very good.

I'm sure Gershon will come back a changed man.

Fri 25 Aug: Gershon called me in to see him at noon. He had a bottle of Sauternes and a plate of pâté de foie gras on his desk. He looked very happy. "I love France," he said. "BUT I HATE THE FRENCH!"

His demeanour changed abruptly. He ranted and raved for hours, and I found it almost impossible to understand what he was saying. But there were phrases like "supercilious bureaucrats", "ridiculous xenophobic conditions" and "stuff them if that's what they want", which made me think that the meeting had not gone very well. Piecing it all together, I gathered that the French did not welcome the idea of AFFE competing with French banks for retail business and had suggested that "Monsieur Gershon come back some other time".

Gershon stood up and flung my paper across the desk. "A more telling argument for quitting this appalling Union, I have never encountered," he yelled. He got out his cheque book and added: "I'm sending £1,000 to the eurosceptic campaign right now. And don't ever mention MiFID to me again."

I shall obviously have to take a leaf out of Brussels's book and approach this issue in more devious ways.

Parquet

Gershon blogs:

Mon 21 Aug: Among this week's many unattractive prospects is a visit to England's traditional enemy – La Belle France (for it is she). AFFE is applying for a retail licence and, although there is apparently no mention of the requirement in the requisite directive, it seems that the CEO of the company making the application is required to attend in person in order to genuflect at the tomb of the unknown collaborator, or some such thing. Frankly I'm astonished that any of our European Community partners are available given that it's August – shouldn't they be wiping the garlicky oil off their mouths while preening themselves on the beach?

Tues 22 Aug: Ritual humiliation aside, this French thing should be a good opportunity to broaden our retail deposit base – always handy when wholesale markets cut up rough as they are now doing. What seems to be missing from the operational review is any discussion of the compliance aspects of the project. A call to Parquet finds him elusive as ever. Pauline is there, however. Apparently she can "hardly move in this heat". What, I wonder, is the required temperature?

Wed 23 Aug: The brief window that opened between the monthly human resources meeting (Bridget believes the bank should be more inclusive) and boarding the Eurostar is filled by a visit from Parquet who has written a paper. It does not deal with the compliance aspects of our application. Ostensibly about MiFID, it is a paean to European culture. "Not many people," enthuses Parquet in person, "think of Beethoven as German," I must be one of the few, then.

Thurs 24 Aug: Hateful day following a magnificent dinner last night. The witty and urbane companions of the night before are transmogrified into the devious and mendacious bureaucrats they always were. One hundred euros says our application was dead on arrival.

Fri 25 Aug: We were promised a speedy decision and certainly get it. Surprise! Our application has been turned down. You might almost think that it was a foregone conclusion – surely not. Moved by I know not what, I decide to call in Parquet and show him the error of his ways, viz. that liking French food and German music is entirely compatible with wishing to see the great European plot and all its works consigned to outer darkness. Uncomprehending, nervous and faintly resentful he slinks away. As I pass their office on my way to leave the building I see Parquet – apparently slumped over his desk. Pauline raises a podgy hand in farewell. Heigh ho.

Gershon

Compliance Professional of the Year

Parquet blogs:

Mon 22 Jan 2007: I see that the FSA has launched an investigation into leaks about takeovers. Quite right too. It's shocking how people take advantage of secrets about forthcoming bids to profit from share movements. It corrupts the market. But it's also a sad reflection on the state of Compliance in the City. Good Chinese walls should take care of that. Fortunately, at AFFE, we have excellent Internal Security, and there's never been a problem.

Still, if the FSA is sniffing around, this might be a good moment to run a check and a refresher.

I see, incidentally, that nominations are being sought for this year's Compliance Officer of the Year Award. I must try and drum up some support among my colleagues. I'm sure I stand a good chance of winning, specially after all the work I've done implementing Basel 2 and MiFID.

Tues 23 Jan: I've scheduled a meeting of department heads for tomorrow morning to discuss internal security. I'm afraid it will take some time. This is not a matter that can be waved through in five minutes. I'll also distribute a brief on the FSA investigation to make them all sit up and take note. I've asked Pauline, my deputy, to arrange wall charts and organograms – and a plentiful supply of pads and pens.

I'm also pressing on with the award nominations. They have to be in by the end of the week. I know that Compliance Officers are not the most popular people in the bank (!). But that's usually because they're doing a good job, and I'm sure my colleagues understand and respect me for that. I put in a few calls, but no one's got back to me yet.

Wed 24 Jan: I think the Compliance Meeting went very well. It took rather longer than I thought – three hours – but there was a lot to get through. Controls on IT, physical access to the corporate finance department, treatment of market sensitive information, lines of command, disciplinary procedures etc. At the end I had to get them all to sign an attendance register.

It's amazing how it all mounts up. I sensed a certain impatience in the air, and mobile phones were ringing constantly. But we covered a lot of ground, and all the important people were there. Gershon even dropped by, but his phone rang pretty soon and he had to leave. Pity. I'd like him to see what a thorough job I'm doing.

I took the liberty of slipping in a small request at the end for award nominations. I'm sure they will respond, having seen how efficiently I handled the meeting. After all, it's for their own good. They were a bit offhand though.

Thurs 25 Jan: *1pm.* No nominations came in by lunchtime. I expect they're all busy checking out security in their departments. Maybe tonight.

6pm. Horrors. The late edition of the *Evening Standard* had a headline "AFFE fingered in FSA leaks probe". I couldn't believe it. According to the paper, AFFE has been identified as one of the main sources of leaks in the City. Gershon was on the phone immediately. "What's all this?" I had to deny all knowledge: the FSA had never spoken to me about it. I rang up my contact at the FSA. She said it was all confidential, and she couldn't comment. Stumped.

Midnight. Up all evening chasing around for leaks, with Gershon hounding me. I badgered each department head for details of all the deals they had been involved with. If I have my suspicions, they lie in the direction of the trading room: the equity dealers will do anything to turn a buck. But corporate finance isn't that clean either. They can't re-sist the temptation to boast about their deals – and make a "small" profit on the side. The more I think about it, the more I suspect that everyone is in on the act in some way. When you're talking billion dollar deals, the flesh is weak indeed. My eyelids are drooping.

Fri 26 Jan: *10am.* Got in late feeling very bleary. News of the FSA probe on the front page of all the papers. Popular revenge for all those massive Christmas bonuses. Everyone else looking pretty bleary too. Gershon calls a meeting of dept. heads – and me. Gives me a dressing down in front of all the others for "an effing public relations disaster".

Noon. FSA just put out a statement saying that their investigation is "focusing broadly on many institutions, not one in particular". Small compensation. Why didn't they say that yesterday? Got a call from my FSA contact. "Sorry I couldn't say anything," she said. "It's so sensitive. But I can tell you that AFFE's not a prime suspect." Phew! I rush in to tell Gershon, who just glowers.

4pm. The award nominations have to be in by 6pm, and I haven't received a single one. Still, I gather that judges go by the quality of the nominations, not the number. Also, you are allowed to nominate yourself. Ah well…

Parquet

Gershon blogs:

Mon 22 Jan: Thank goodness the bonus season is over for another year – whoever said that the politics (or should that be the journalism?) of envy was dead? After weeks of press coverage of "multimillion pound bonuses" everyone in the country, including most of the City, feels hard done by in spite of living through one of the longest periods of prosperity in history.

Tues 23 Jan: Against my better judgment I take a call from a hack on the subject of, guess what, City bonuses. I give said hack the well rehearsed lines about free markets, global meritocracy etc. "But," the reptile insists, is something not amiss when he can only afford an artisan's cottage in west London in spite of writing for one of the world's most prestigious organs (sic)? I retort that writing a weekly column for a paper with an almost exclusively UK readership of a few hundred thousand hardly puts him very far up the global pecking order and regret it immediately. Hell hath no fury…

Wed 24 Jan: Amid all the regular New Year kerfuffle I have become uneasily aware of increased activity in the compliance area. A rare sighting of the ample figure of Pauline, Assistant Compliance Officer, actually on her feet for once (in this case discontentedly hauling a box of pencils across the foyer) is the first indication. A bright greeting from Parquet is the second unwelcome sign. I think of asking but instead decide to wait for the phone to ring.

Walking past the big meeting room on the way to lunch I pop my head in to see that Parquet has got the whole department pinned down while he discusses his role in approving disciplinary procedures – no role at all as far as I'm concerned.

The audience looks thoroughly bored and resentful while Pauline sprawls grumpily at the front, wolfing chocolate biscuits. Still – do them a bit of good to understand what real suffering is.

Thurs 25 Jan: I knew it. "AFFE fingered in FSA leaks probe" sings the headline in the late edition. Temporarily forgetting my selfless attempt to enlighten the Great British Journalist I fall back on the old equation; Increased compliance activity = incipient compliance disaster. I ring Parquet, get Pauline (what's she eating now?). Apparently "we don't know anything about it". No surprises there, then.

Fri 26 Jan: Call meeting of department heads to see if we really do

have a serious problem. Doesn't sound like it. Parquet arrives late with no proper explanation. On our way out he asks me to nominate him for some award he has decided he deserves. Thank goodness it's the weekend.
Gershon

Meeting the headhunter

Parquet blogs:

Mon 26 Feb: I got a call from a headhunter this morning. Not something that happens every day, I have to admit. The man said he was looking for someone to take up a very senior financial regulatory position. The successful candidate would have to have "extensive experience of international regulation and compliance, with a proven track record". The salary would be in six figures (six figures!). Was I interested?

I could hardly stay in my seat. But like all compliance officers, I'm good at looking po-faced, so I said casually: "Maybe". I added, "but I'm very happy here," (what nonsense!). He asked me to think about it, and he'd call back in a couple of days.

This was just the tonic I needed. I've been very low recently. I failed to win an award or even a commendation at last month's Compliance Officer of the Year ceremony, despite the fantastic job I did on Basel 2 implementation for AFFE.

Also, the board is nagging me to finish my report on MiFID. I just can't make any progress at all. It's the most brain-breaking subject, and it's wearing me down. I've asked Pauline, my deputy, to get some stuff off the web, but I think her brain needs defragmenting.

Tues 27 Feb: Deirdre was tremendously excited by my news when I got home last night. She agrees totally that I'm seriously under-appreciated at AFFE, and if someone wants to poach me then I'm all for it, and so is she.

I'd hardly been at my desk a few minutes when the phone rang. It was Gershon. "Where's that MiFID report?" he asked sharply. I was so buoyed up by the thought of a new job that I almost told him to get lost (Imagine that!). "In good time," I said, trying to sound offhand.

I always keep a close eye on the jobs market and I know that de-mand for good compliance people has gone through the roof. There are websites now where you can see exactly what MiFID skills are be-ing sought, and how much they pay. Good compliance officers can get £75,000 easily. But the headhunter said six figures!

I suddenly had a thought. He couldn't be sounding me out for a top job at the FSA, could he? I went hot and cold all over. What a fantastic idea! I could become a serious public figure, make a real difference…

But if I'm to get anywhere, I've got to be on top of MiFID. On with the dreaded task. Pauline has downloaded 547 pages from the FSA website.

Wed 28 Feb: I spent the morning in a state of high excitement wait-ing for the headhunter to call back. He came through at noon. "Well?" he asked. "I'd need to know more, much more," I said. "A drink this evening?" he suggested. "Fine," I replied. He proposed The Sauterelle in the Royal Exchange, "upstairs where we can be discreet. They do good dry martinis."

"Perfect," I said, even though I hadn't a clue where he was talking about. But I'll find it. Anything to get out of this place. I left Pauline to draft a section on multilateral trading facilities and post-trade transparency.

Thurs 1 Mar: It wasn't exactly what I was expecting. It turns out that the Bucharest Stock Exchange want to beef up their compliance function now that Romania has joined the EU. They're prepared to pay good money for someone to come over for a couple of years to oversee implementation.

I was doing my best to hide my disappointment when there was suddenly a slap on my shoulder. It was Gershon! "Hi Parquet! Fancy seeing you at the headhunters' watering hole! Not thinking of quitting are you?" I sank through the floor.

When I got in this morning, I rang the headhunter up. "Count me out," I said.

Now I really must get on with the MiFID report and get Gershon off my back.

Fri 2 Mar: First thing this morning, Gershon called me in. He was clutching a sheaf of papers from the FSA. He said: "The trouble with you, Parquet, is that you're the only person in this place who knows a damn thing about this stuff – and I go and catch you with a head hunter. What's he offering?"

"Six figures," I replied.

"I'll think about it," he said.

When I got back to my desk I noticed that Pauline was Googling Bucharest. "Holiday?" I asked with a grin. "Maybe," she said with a yawn.

Parquet

Gershon blogs

Mon 26 Feb: Monthly economic briefing presided over by the emaciated figure of Wharton Graff, our resident economist. In addition to his signature Ivy League-style horn rimmed spectacles he is wearing a jaunty bow tie. He looks utterly ridiculous as usual. In his discussion of the UK economy we learn that, a) The level of immigration is unknown, and b) VAT fraud is on such a scale that the trade statistics are make-believe, so c) There is no earthly chance of knowing what is going on.

Tues 27 Feb: How very different in the public sector. Down at the Wharf certainty reigns as another confident and lengthy missive from the FSA flops on to my desk, which reminds me – where is Parquet's MiFID report? A phone call elicits one of those tiresomely typical "no hurry" Parquet responses – where one is not quite sure whether he has

failed to understand the question or is being deliberately obstructive.
He's got to go.

Wed 28 Feb: A visit to Parquet's lair (why is it me that feels uncomfortable?) only confirms yet another of his unexplained absences. I mean, where on earth does he go? Pauline, however, is present. Something has obviously got her going; she spins round on her chair as I come in – a previously unrecorded feat of athleticism. I assume that closing down the webpage which was engrossing her has something to do with it. She has no idea where Parquet might be and seems quite surprised that I should ask.

Thurs 1 Mar: Despairing of ever getting rid of Parquet, Pauline and all their works, I have thought of a cunning plan. Johnny C (whose career commenced as the dimmest boy in the school, progressing via the stupidest subaltern in the household cavalry to the richest and most successful headhunter in the City) owes me one.
   A debt he can now honourably (-ish) discharge by headhunting Parquet – ideally placing him with a competitor I regard with particular hostility, although at this point I'll settle for pretty much anything. Anyway, who should I see as I walk into the Sauterelle to meet Johnny, but Parquet himself. Is this where he goes during those long and mysterious absences?

Fri 2 Mar: I call Parquet and raise the subject of our encounter at the Sauterelle "OK Arnold, what are they offering?" "Six figures," he replies. Now there's precision and professionalism for you. Would that be 100,000 or 999,999 Lei, do you suppose?
Gershon

~

The first signs of serious strain in the system are apparent by April 2007. In the middle of the month, New Century Financial, a specialist US subprime lender, files for bankruptcy, an intimation of much worse to come. At AFFE the introduction of a new "No Smoking" policy is exercising the minds of senior management.

~

Health and safety issues

Parquet blogs:

Mon 26 Mar: Trouble ahead. The anti-smoking law (which I hugely welcome) comes into force on July 1st – and we need a policy. Trouble is, Gershon enjoys a good cigar (there's a contradiction in terms), and I know he sneaks on to the roof garden outside his office for a puff.

I examine the new regulation – is a roof garden part of the "work-space" and hence a no-smoking area? The definition says that the space must be largely enclosed by walls and a roof. I'm certain that Gershon will claim that it is open to the elements.

But we can't allow exceptions or privileges. The company already has enough trouble with crowds of smokers hanging around outside the main entrance, disfiguring the building. They will now be made to "move along", as policemen say.

I shall have to play this one carefully. My MiFID report will have to wait.

Tues 27 Mar: Draft smoking policy is nearly complete. I have decided to be firm and insert the phrase "including roof gardens" in the definition of areas covered by our new regulations. Gershon won't like it. But this is my opportunity to make a small contribution to the elimination of this detestable habit.

I emailed the draft to Gershon just before leaving this evening. I expect sparks to fly tomorrow.

Wed 28 Mar: *Noon.* Quite extraordinary! Gershon greeted me with a wave in the corridor this morning, apparently full of the joys of spring. Perhaps he hasn't read the draft yet…

4pm. Got a call from Gershon's PA to come in tomorrow at 10.30 am to discuss the smoking policy. I must brace myself for a tough confrontation. This is not the moment to weaken. Gershon can be ruthless – and devious – about getting his way.

Thurs 29 Mar: Got in early. I asked Pauline, my deputy, to contact the printers and order 200 signs with the words "No Smoking. It is against the law to smoke on these premises". The law says that the signs have to be A5 size. But I've decided to go one better and make them A4. Our workspaces – the dealing rooms, for instance – are very big and some of the staff won't be able to read the signs if they're too small (the signs I mean).

12.30pm. Even more extraordinary! I went in to see Gershon and we had a very amicable discussion. He seemed to think the regulations were very good and clear and said he looked forward to seeing me enforce them. I wasn't used to this sort of treatment and I searched for a note of sarcasm in his voice, but couldn't detect any.

He only had a couple of questions. Did the signs really have to be as big as A4? He thought they would look ugly. To show that I was a reasonable man, I agreed to cut them back to A5. A small concession to keep Gershon on board!

His other question was merely a point of clarification. He asked if it was correct that these rules only applied to the work premises, not to staff living quarters. Yes, I replied. What people did in the privacy of their own living quarters was entirely up to them. (I was going to add "like destroying their lungs" – but tact restrained me.)

Fri 30 Mar: Pauline and I spent most of the day drafting a new Rule Book on Smoking for the staff. I'm very conscious of the huge amount of new rules that have been introduced recently, so I'm keeping it short – about 20 pages. I shall also have to ask each member of the staff to sign a Declaration that they have read them and are aware of the penalties. I know all that is tedious but it could save a lot of unpleasantness later.

We were disturbed in the afternoon by a team of workmen who began banging and drilling in the board room down the hall. I went down to ask them to keep quiet. To my amazement, I found them redecorating it in homely style and installing a living room suite.

I went to Gershon's PA and asked: "What on earth's going on?" She shrugged. "The board of directors has decided to lease the board room to Mr Gershon as his private accommodation. It's his to do with as he pleases."

I was mystified. Why would the board want to do that? Very convenient for Gershon, of course, but highly extravagant with prime office space worth a bomb.

Since the noise didn't stop, Pauline and I decided to go home early, with a good week's work behind us. Must get on with that MiFID report.
Parquet

Gershon blogs:

Mon 26 Mar: Slightly disconcerted to see MiFID referred to in the *FT* as the "biggest change since Big Bang". Somehow I seem to have missed something, in spite of innumerable requests made of Parquet and the piles of guff he prints off the internet when really hard pressed. Could it really be that important? What do he and Pauline (not to mention the teams of people he would hire, given half a chance) actually do all day?

Tues 27 Mar: The answer to my rhetorical question arrives with mocking swiftness. The answer is that, in preference to trying to understand MiFID, Parquet and co. have been working out how to enforce the new policy on smoking in the workplace – a project rich with opportunities for indulging moral superiority and self-importance.

Who will rid me of this appalling individual? Not John Sutton to whom he reports directly, that's for sure. I made a high-level pass over the target at last week's senior managers' meeting only for our very own blunt Northerner ("Where I come from, Edward, we tell it straight") to let me know that he regarded the Compliance function as being under his personal protection. Why, for goodness sake?

Wed 28 Mar: I had hoped that my roof terrace might have, so to speak, slipped under the radar (the little creep seems to have driven me into Battle of Britain mode). Not so – the attention to detail that seems to elude Parquet when looking at the outpourings of the FSA did not desert him on this crucial mission. However, I have a plan – the board room becomes my private apartment to which I can retire and enjoy my occasional cigar. It doesn't quite amount to my loyal knights cutting him down on the steps of the canteen but it runs a good second.

Thurs 29 Mar: Parquet is beside himself with excitement. Size of No Smoking signs. Precise wording of No Smoking signs. Typeface of No Smoking signs. Position of No Smoking Signs. Policy on Staff signing off that No Smoking signs have been read and understood. And all to no avail.

Fri 30 Mar: Leave at lunchtime to go to the country. Share lift down with Pauline and her signature scent of cheap sweets. Beware my lovely – if smoking is banned the Fat Police are not far behind.
Gershon

~

A visit from the noble knight

Parquet blogs:
Mon 28 May: Big week this. We have Sir Callum McCarthy, the chairman of the FSA, coming to lunch on Friday and we need to be armed with good topics for discussion – and a few light-hearted titbits to keep the conversation going! It's taken months to set this up but it's a real opportunity to share ideas with the great man.

The trouble is that Gershon isn't very keen on regulation and he'll need a good briefing beforehand. Fortunately, I attended an FSA conference down at Canary Wharf only a few weeks ago where I picked up the latest gen. It also gave me a chance to see Sir Callum in the flesh for the first time. I was really impressed. He was all charm and self-effacingness, not at all the almighty financial regulator. In fact I'd describe him as a true gent. He made me really proud to be in the Compliance Business.

His speech was about the FSA's move towards principles-driven regulation, something which I wholeheartedly approbate. All part of Sir Callum's drive for light-touch regulation – or "sensible proportionate regulation" as he prefers to call it. Such a way with words.

Tues 29 May: There was a large and angry crowd of visitors around the reception desk when I got in this morning (slightly late, I confess, because of late-night research on my MiFID paper).

I quickly ascertained the problem. It was 10am, a time when a wave of visitors arrives for appointments. The queues for elevators were bad and one visitor got hurt in the crush. Maybe the answer is to stagger visitor appointments so that they don't all come on the hour. We can't risk unseemly scenes in the entrance hall.

Started researching a brief for Gershon. I looked up the FSA's regulatory principles on its website. There are 11 of them, a rather odd number. For tidiness sake, I think there should be 12, and I'd like to propose to Sir Callum something along the lines of "The Compliance Officer is central to the effective implementation of sensible proportionate regulation, and should be accorded appropriate status". I'm sure he'd see the sense of that.

Wed 30 May: Another horrific melee at the reception desk. I must have a word with Security about my staggering idea because I know the problem is only going to get worse.

Got down to writing the brief for Gershon: a bit of background on Sir

Callum, an outline of the FSA's objectives, the shift to principles-driven regulation, "Treating Customers Fairly", details of Brussels' Financial Services Action Plan, MiFID, the Payments Services Directive, the Transparency Directive, T2S, Basel 2 and a few other bits and pieces. I'm afraid the brief became rather longer than I intended but we can't let our chief executive appear ignorant in the company of our Chief Regulator!

Thurs 31 May: Had a good meeting with Tony Imbroglio, the head of Security. He used to be in the football crowd control business, so he was full of ideas. His proposal was to allocate visitors 15-minute slots to spread out arrivals. If someone arrived early or late, he would be told to wait until there was a vacant slot. Very simple, really.

We decided to implement the scheme straight away, so I circulated a memo to department heads and gave strict instructions to the staff at reception to stick to the rules, and deal politely but firmly with visitors. I know this all sounds incredibly officious but I see no alternative. If it works for air traffic control, it can work for AFFE!

Gershon called me in this afternoon to talk about the lunch. He came straight to the point. "What are we going to talk about that's not incredibly dull?" I pushed my brief across his desk. "Plenty in there," I said. Gershon waved me away with what sounded like a sigh.

Fri 1 June: The first I heard about the disaster was around 12.45 when I got a call from reception. "There's a Mr McCarthy here who's arrived for a 1pm lunch appointment. I've told him he'll have to wait until 1pm because that's his arrival slot."

I let out a yelp and dashed to the elevator. It took an age to reach the ground floor, where I rushed over to reception. "Where is he?" I asked. The girl replied: "He went back outside to sit in his car." I ran out into the street and found the car. I was terrified that he would be angry and irritated. But what a gent! He smiled and said: "How nice to see you."

I won't dwell on the lunch. I was so put out that I forgot to make my 12th principle proposal, and Gershon, for some reason, said very little. But Sir Callum was all charm and chat. "Thank you so much for asking me," he said as he left. "We do like to listen and learn."

Parquet

Gershon blogs:

Mon 28 May: I bump into Parquet in the corridor outside the board-room. Why is he always out and about for apparently no purpose? He has some exciting news. Apparently we are to be visited by a "person of considerable eminence". From his expression this must be a visit from heaven, the Archangel Gabriel at least if not the Almighty himself. Sadly (or is that "fortunately"?) it transpires that the person is "only" Sir Callum McCarthy, knight of the FSA.

Tues 29 May: In preparation for the meeting I phone Parquet to ask him to prepare a bit of background so at least there is something to talk about at what threatens (to put it mildly) to be a lunch characterised by longueurs. As usual he is enjoying one of his unexplained absences. Pauline answers the phone, her mouth stuffed full of something or other. If I understand her muffled response correctly she has kindly agreed to pass the message on.

Wed 30 May: Total chaos in the reception area this morning presided over as usual by our heavily coiffed and (as far as I know) self-styled "Head of Security", Antonio Imbroglio. He has two modes. The more common of the two is a condition of complete inertia in which his heavily lidded eyes hardly move except to follow any half-presentable female as she crosses the entrance foyer. The other is one of barely suppressed fury when he is called upon actually to do something. How difficult can it be to get all-comers to write Mickey Mouse in a book before giving them a badge allowing them a free run of the building?

Thurs 31 May: An unwelcome visit from Parquet (is there any other kind?) sees him carrying a vast file consisting of unedited internet content laboriously, unnecessarily and expensively printed out. The sole point of his simple brief – to provide something to talk about at lunchtime – lost.

Fri 1 June: Any goodwill we might have generated from McCarthy's visit is entirely dissipated by sending him back to his car and making him wait for his "arrival slot". I am very annoyed when I go to speak to Imbroglio, but that pales into insignificance compared with the rage I experience when I discover that the "new security system" was master-minded by Parquet. Why can't he just go and boil his head?
Gershon

By July the trickle of bad news from the US housing market has started to increase. House prices are now falling, meaning that the second line of defence when a borrower defaults – to sell the house to recover the debt – has started to give way. Markets become more and more nervous of the lower-rated tranches of mortgage securitisations – the ones that are first in line to absorb losses from mortgages which aren't repaid in full. Bear Stearns (later to be the first big firm to be rescued) announces it is closing two hedge funds that invested in mortgage-backed paper. Investors face a total loss.

A month later the French bank BNP suspends withdrawals from two of its funds, citing a "total lack of liquidity". The process of the system seizing up begins with a vengeance in August and the Great Credit Crunch begins. Over the next two years more and more instruments will become near impossible to turn into cash. The ECB, the Fed and the Bank of Japan all intervene to provide emergency liquidity. The Fed cuts the discount rate, beginning the process which, over the next eighteen months, will effectively lower official interest rates worldwide to zero.

~

Compliance to the rescue!

Parquet blogs:
Mon 25 June: The economic outlook looks very black. Almost every day the newspapers have horror stories about markets collapsing and company earnings heading down the tubes. What disasters await us? America imploding, China going up in flames, the housing market falling in on itself? I dread to think.

My problem is that there are people in this bank who are still in a state of total denial. Gershon goes around looking as if it's all sunshine, and our equity research people keep cranking out "buy" recommendations on the flakiest stocks. The last thing we want is so-called "rainmakers" in the corporate finance and trading departments pocketing million dollar bonuses for pushing us into subprime lending.

I feel it's my duty to cool things down a bit in this bank, but I'm not sure how.

Tues 26 June: Inspiration! I got a call from the FSA this morning reminding me that our implementation of the Basel 2 Capital Adequacy Requirements must be complete by the end of the year – only six months away, which is no time at all, really. As part of the process, we will have to stress test our loan and trading portfolios to make sure that we meet all the rules.

This is very timely. It means that I can insist to management that we create a whole range of disaster scenarios and then apply them to our portfolios to see how well they stand up. Gershon and Co will soon see that they're fooling themselves if they think everything is yankee doodle.

Annoyingly, I ripped my trousers just now as I was settling down at my desk to design stress scenarios. It was a projecting screw. Fortunately, I keep a small toolkit in my drawer to deal with these eventualities. I have extracted the screw and thrown it away. But the trousers are finished. I shall have to go home.

The MiFID report can wait.

Wed 27 June: I'm having great fun designing disaster scenarios. My central scenario is built round the collapse of the US mortgage market and a complete wipe-out of the equity and bond markets. Derivative markets are in chaos and nobody is quoting prices. I'm calling it "Men in rags". I think that will really test our risk management capableness.

I've got another scenario based on a terrorist attack on IT systems that destroys all our computers and telephones and leaves us totally in the dark with all communication and data lost. It'll be interesting to see how our business continuation people respond! It's called "Men in black".

My favourite, though, is one where a disgruntled employee infiltrates a deadly virus into the air conditioning system and kills all the people in the corporate finance and trading departments. The only people in the building who escape are the Compliance Team and all hope is pinned on them... It's called "Men in shining armour".

Thurs 28 June: *am.* I've fixed a meeting with Gershon this afternoon to go through my scenarios. I know he won't like them because they'll put a damper on things. But it's not my job to make life a bed of roses

for him – a bed of thorns more like! It won't help that the new anti-smoking regulations come into force today. Without his cigar, he'll be in a bad mood.

I printed up my scenarios and attached the FSA's guidance notes on stress testing to send round to Gershon as a brief ahead of the meeting. It made quite a bulky package but at least I can be sure I've covered all the bases.

pm. I was right about Gershon. He didn't even wait for me to come round to see him. He stormed over to my cubicle clutching my package. "Parquet," he said. "If we're stress testing this business, I want a reality check, not pulp fiction," and flung the package on to my desk.

Unfortunately, the sudden weight of the brief caused my desk to collapse, bringing down the partition wall, and knocking over my computer. There was a tremendous crash followed by an awful silence. Everyone in the room looked up.

"Ha!" shouted Gershon. "You couldn't stress test a piece of office furniture!" And he vanished back up the hall, leaving me surrounded in debris.

I decided to go home early.

Fri 29 June: In reassembling my desk this morning, I discovered that the screw that I had removed was crucial to holding it together. How stupid of the manufacturers to imagine that it would stand up to the rough and tumble of a busy office. It's not my fault that Compliance work generates a lot of paper.

In the afternoon, Gershon circulated a note to staff saying that AFFE's first half earnings were at a new high, thanks to a strong performance by the corporate finance and trading departments.

I know it can't last. I just know…

Parquet

Gershon blogs:

Mon 25 June: An old but truthful saying about markets is that "things go on for longer and end more suddenly than anyone expects". The appalling spectacle of Hedgestock – a "Woodstock" style event featuring live music (and a Bentley dealership) – is now nearly a year ago. This had me seriously worried at the time but here we still are, hardly damp from the complete collapse of the US subprime market and now, apparently, not a cloud in the sky.

Tues 26 June: Lunch with the company lawyers. Robert is very busy. "Good news," I suggest. Ever cautious, he reminds me that last time they had this much work – 2000 – he saw the value of his pension fund plunge over the subsequent three years. Hmmmm.

Wed 27 June: A long discussion at today's Risk Committee about the likely official response to a market dislocation. All we could come up with was a reduction in interest rates by the central banks. With banking supervision now shared between competing bureaucracies and no control over how many Mongolian Tugriks have been swapped into the currency of which they are the appointed custodians, it's about all they can do. "Big hat, no cattle," as they say in Texas. No intelligent input from Compliance of course.

Thurs 28 June: Passed Pauline in the corridor carrying a bouquet of flowers. I can only assume she bought them for herself. There again it's hard to imagine her wasting money that could have been spent on sweets so perhaps she stole them. My desk is scarcely visible under an enormous pile of stuff from Parquet. My heart gives a little leap. The MiFID report has finally arrived! I have misjudged him!

The moment of ecstasy is – as the poet said – only too brief. The document purports to be an attempt to stress test the bank's risk systems.

What has in fact happened is that in the dark hours, Parquet's muse has visited him with an idea for a story in which a compliance officer (who could it be, we wonder?) saves the world.

It's called, I can hardly bring myself to write this, "Men in shining armour". Why should I be subjected to this garbage? I cross the hallway to his den and dump it on his desk which rather gratifyingly collapses. My guffaw is cut short by a dirty look from Ms Obergruppenführer Bridget, head of Human Resources and author of *Respect at Work 2007*, who happens to be passing. I wave back.

Fri 29 June: Quarterly results presentation. Eight bells and all's still well.

Gershon

Market seizure

Parquet blogs:

Mon 27 Aug: Back from two weeks camping on the Continent to find the markets in a state of complete turmoil, and all my worst fears come true. Prices are plummeting, people are staring ashen-faced at their screens. But there's also an eerie silence because NOTHING'S HAPPENING! The whole business has completely clammed up.

With everything in paralysis and disarray, it's obviously up to the Compliance Department to show leadership. I must organise an emergency meeting of the Risk Committee, order more copies of the Compliance Manual, galvanize the bank. Otherwise we shall fail by default.

The papers and the TV are absolutely full of it. Nobody has a clue what's going on. It could just be a blip or the worst crisis in decades. I have to admit that I don't completely understand how credit default swaps work. But they're the heart of the problem, and need to be tackled head on. Will mug them up tonight.

Tues 28 Aug: I have sent memos to all Department Heads asking for a full update on their exposures so that we can get a grip on things. Next, we shall tot up our losses and sell out of the worst situations. Then... well, we'll decide. But we can't possibly allow this to go on a minute longer than necessary. Above all, we must be in full Compliance with all the FSA's regulations on financial soundness.

Pauline has distributed copies of the Compliance Manual to all senior AFFE staff with a covering note to direct any questions to me.

I must fix a meeting with Gershon. He's probably paralysed too.

Wed 29 Aug: "Too busy to see me!" That's what Gershon's PA said to me. I can't believe it! The ship is foundering, there's no one on the bridge, and the captain declines to see the one person who's showing any initiative. I insist on seeing him and push my way into his office.

Instead of finding a morgue, I discover that it is full of people crowding round a table covered in papers. I imagine for a moment that they are studying the Compliance Manual, but no, it is something else.

Gershon ignores me, and drones on about credit lines and third tier assets and access to central bank liquidity. He obviously hasn't a clue what is going on. He straightens up and asks: "Any questions?" I plunge in immediately: "What are we doing about the crisis?" but find myself ignored. This is obviously worse than I feared.

Maybe I shall have to seize control of the bank.

Thurs 30 Aug: Coming to work, everything seemed so weird. On the one hand, all the media are screaming crisis. Governments are racing to prop up markets, and everyone is in a daze. But on the other, the trains are still running and the shops are still selling sandwiches. Life goes on. I suppose it always does, even in the financial equivalent of Hiroshima.

Today, I shall draw up a summary of all the initiatives we are taking in Compliance to ensure that the bank sticks to the rules. This is the moment I have been preparing for: the crisis that strikes at the heart of the business. Only I (and my immediate colleagues) can keep the vital organs going. AFFE will be judged by the rest of the market on its Compliance record.

I'm still not quite on top of credit default swaps, but getting there.

Fri 31 Aug: Gershon still refuses to see me. He's obviously totally shell-shocked. I've no alternative but to call my contact at the FSA and alert her to the vacuum that goes by the name of AFFE management.

She sounded a bit weary. I explained to her that the bank was in danger of drifting rudderless in the maelstrom but that I was doing my best to enforce the capital adequacy regulations.

"The what?" she asked, with a laugh. "The capital adequacy regulations," I repeated.

"Stuff those," she replied. "We're way past all that. There are no rules any more. We're fighting fires minute by minute. The best thing you can do is go out into the street with a begging bowl. Sorry I've got someone else on the line." She hung up.

I was flabbergasted. Not only have the markets collapsed, but the rules have been destroyed as well. That means there's nothing left at all.

I felt very sick and decided to leave early.

Parquet

Gershon blogs:

Mon 27th Aug: Banking life as we know it has ground to a halt. Previously liquid securities are now impossible to trade and the entire industry appears to spend its time in meetings deciding how far to cut agreed counterparty limits.

Tues 28th Aug: One of the things which makes this situation so intractable is that there is really nothing in AFFE's modus operandi to help us. The basic assumption underlying our business model is that markets remain open and we can get access to cash by shedding assets – without this ability we constantly run the risk that we might default on a payment – however sound our balance sheet. Discussions with our counterparties get us nowhere, they are in the same position as us, can sympathise but nonetheless the relentless process of cutting credit lines continues.

Wed 29th Aug: The authorities are not much use either. There is no established fire drill for a problem on this scale – maybe there is for depositary institutions which take deposits from the general public but for AFFE it's not even clear who we should talk to. The entire senior management group is in my conference room when the door opens and Parquet walks in. He is fresh from an extended holiday and has come to give us the benefit of his insights. In particular he wants to know what we are doing about the crisis. B*****d if I know.

Thur 30th Aug: Finally a little bit of traction with the authorities and some liquidity support is forthcoming – the trouble is no one knows where they stand and they too are making up the rules as they go along. How much the assets are worth, once our greatest concern, is now largely irrelevant since there's no market for them.

Fri 31st Aug: The only thing to hope for is that this is just a temporary panic – after all, we've seen that in the past, after LTCM went down for example. Here's hoping.
Gershon

2

The populace
takes to the streets

September 2007 saw the storming of Northern Rock – the first run on a British bank since World War One. Although it preceded the major failures of the credit crunch by more than a year, the television pictures of queues of depositors outside Northern Rock branches are perhaps the iconic images of the early stages of the banking crisis. In reality Northern Rock was relatively free of the more exotic financial vices which later came to be blamed for the debacle. A fairly boring organisation from the north of England, its raciness was largely confined to aggressive lending practises in the UK mortgage market and its chief executive, while very well paid by most people's standards, would not merit even a mention in the Greedy Banker's Hall of Infamy. In what was shortly to become a habit, the Bank of England provided emergency support.

Across the Atlantic, the Fed cut its main rate to 4.75% – the first cut of many. Two months later, the Bank of England followed with a reduction of its lending rate to 5.5% with worries about inflation giving way to fears of something worse. Over the next two months the scale of the subprime problem started to be revealed. In early October, Citigroup revealed losses of $3.1bn. A fortnight later it revealed further losses of \$5.9bn. Within six months its stated losses would exceed \$60bn. Central Banks co-ordinated operations to provide liquidity to the system and temporarily succeed in lowering inter bank rates. Experts explained the difference between insolvent (bust) and illiquid (short of cash) to anyone who was prepared to listen.

Five minutes of fame

Parquet blogs:

Mon 24 Sep: I have to reveal a deadly secret: I am a big saver in Northern Rock: about £25,000 actually. It's most of my life savings.

So imagine my horror when I saw the TV screens reporting a run on the bank. This put me in a terrible dilemma. As someone in the compliance business, I know quite a bit about managing bank panics. It's all in the mind really. Northern Rock was perfectly solvent: just suffering a temporary liquidity problem. So I told myself to sit tight and stay calm.

But it wasn't easy. Hour after hour the TV news showed queues of people all over the country waiting to get their money out. I also heard the governor of the Bank of England, no less, saying that it would be wrong for the country to bail out bad banks: sets the wrong tone, he said. Normally, I would be right behind him on that one: once you bail one bank out, where's an end of it? But I began to get edgy.

I must have betrayed my worries. Gershon came past and said: "Cheer up Parquet. You look as if you've got your life savings in Northern Rock."

It was the last straw. There's a Northern Rock branch in Moorgate just around the corner from our offices. So I slipped out during my lunch break, hoping to be back at my desk for the afternoon. No such luck. Everyone else had the same idea, and the queue was a million miles long. Worse than that, there were TV reporters buzzing about like flies, and the last thing I wanted was people at AFFE recognising me. I fled.

That night was agony. I didn't dare tell Deirdre because she's always on at me about saving more money. So imagine my relief when the government announced the next morning that it was guaranteeing Northern Rock's deposits. I could have wept.

Tues 25 Sep: I feel much better having got all that off my chest. But I realise that I allowed my private interests to cloud my judgment about the handling of Northern Rock. Of course it was wrong to bail depositors out. What's the point of having a so-called competitive banking system if the government steps in at the slightest sign of trouble? And what would be the point of compliance?

There's a terrific debate about all this going on in the columns of the *FT*. I really wish I could participate. I'm familiar with all the compliance issues – and I've had direct personal exposure!!!

Wed 26 Sep: I got a call this morning from Bloomberg who are looking for someone to interview on TV about next week's implementation of MiFID – a red letter day in my calendar!! I'm something of an expert on the subject, so I agreed.

I went out to get my hair cut. Bumped into Gershon in the hall on the way back and he made a sarcastic comment about dolling myself up for the media. How does he always know these things? As a Compliance Officer, I'm supposed to be poker-faced.

Thurs 27 Sep: Just back from Bloomberg's offices in Finsbury Square. What an amazing place; full of beautiful people drifting around in a wonderland of winking lights and shiny escalators.

I was greeted by a smart lady who took me downstairs to the TV studio. I felt rather awed by the glamour of the place, but knew it would be wrong to show it. As well as being poker-faced, Compliance Officers are supposed to be unmoved by their surroundings.

They sat me down at a table surrounded by TV cameras (all remote-controlled, I noticed) and wired me up with a lapel mike.

After a chat with the interviewer about the questions he was going to ask, we got going: all pretty routine stuff about MiFID's purpose and the City's preparations, which I answered with ease (and I hope not inordinate length!).

At the end he said: "While you're here Arnold, we should ask you about Northern Rock. As Compliance Officer of a major bank, what do you think went wrong?"

I needed no second bidding. "It was a disgrace," I replied. "The bank should never have been bailed out. I feel very sorry for Mervyn King being forced to do a U-turn by Alastair Darling. It was gross political interference."

"But what about the depositors?" the interviewer asked. I didn't miss a beat. "They've got to take the risk. That's what investment is all about."

As I came back to the office, I felt very pleased that I had been able to overcome my personal feelings and restate what I think is a key principle: no bail-outs!! Someone's got to draw the line…

Fri 28 Sep: I couldn't believe my eyes when I bought my *FT* at the station this morning. There, on the front page: "AFFE slams 'gross political interference'; feels 'sorry' for Bank governor, says depositors should suffer."

I got off at the next station and took the first train back home. The phone has been ringing all day, but I'm not taking any calls. My Northern Rock savings may have to fund a long holiday in Canada.
Parquet

Gershon blogs:

Mon 24 Sep: Some sort of calm has returned to credit markets although not without us all discovering a few unpleasant things about erstwhile friends and neighbours.

No surprise that at the first scent of a kill our noble competitors are transformed into a pack of snarling hyenas but, among others I imagine, I was surprised and dismayed to discover that the Bank of England has no money of its own to speak of and had to trot along to the Treasury.

Amid the rich and varied entrants in the ever hotly contested pub-with-no-beer competition I would never have thought to nominate the Old Lady herself.

No wonder the temporarily embarrassed prefer to apply to the strictly "accountable" ECB where no questions are asked and largesse is lavishly dished out in fully accountable and *communautaire* fashion.

Tues 25 Sep: It is now hardly more than a week until the implementation date of the Markets in Financial Instruments Directive, or MiFID. Our hardworking and overstretched Compliance Department is strangely silent. The desire to pick up the phone and ask Parquet if there is any progress being made battles with the natural desire to avoid anything other than the absolute minimum of contact.

Pauline who described herself as "completely snowed under" when I last had the pleasure of speaking to her, was showing no obvious sign of exertion when last seen. Is this because we are fully prepared?

Wed 26 Sep: A call from Bloomberg TV asking for an interview. With funding still a bit questionable and the environment ever more highly politicised, why on earth would I want to do that? I suggest that our chief compliance officer might perhaps be a better choice. Concise, amusing and telegenic, I cannot recommend him too highly.

Thurs 27 Sep: A circular from "The Conservative Party" asking for money. With the spectacle of boy George up on his hind legs at the party conference promising a spiteful new tax on non-doms still fresh in the mind it goes straight in the bin. The boy wonder needs a lesson in practical finance.

Most people in the UK hate the City but wouldn't much care for our green and pleasant land without it. Sales of financial services abroad pay for a big chunk of imports while taxes levied on them fund the Soviet-style economy of our terminally ungrateful regions.

The advantage of London is that it is much more international than competing centres so why tell the non-doms we're out to get them? Stand by for A. Darling to join the witch hunt.

Fri 28 Sep: A week in which our most revered institutions are revealed to have feet of clay plumbs new depths with today's *Financial Times* ("Europe's Business Newspaper") largely dedicated to the ravings of Parquet. I can't even be bothered to be incensed.

What next for heaven's sake? Pauline as Playmate of the month?
Gershon

The expert investor

Parquet blogs:

Mon 22 Oct: These are amazing times with the banking markets crashing around our ears. But I have more important things to worry about than the credit crunch.

One of them is to vet applications from our private wealth clients to become "expert investors". If they can demonstrate (to me!) that they own more than €500,000 in liquid assets and have strong investment experience, I can authorise them to invest in our "expert funds". These are really high-octane, roller-coaster propositions where they can make a ton of money, or lose it all overnight (a lot of them did in August!)

All our would-be expert investors have to send me full details of their personal wealth, bank statements, copies of their passports, and whatever else I ask for, which means I get to see deep into their private lives (my lips are sealed!) You'd be amazed how much money there is about – and the funny places people tuck it away. There was one man who had every cent locked up in a vault in Geneva because he said that was the only place the rats couldn't get at it.

Up to the middle of this year, I got loads of applications from the "new rich". Fascinating stuff. A lot of them foreign, even women. They all wanted a slice of the private equity action or some red hot hedge fund. But applications have fallen off in the last few weeks. I wonder why…(!!)

Tues 23 Oct: I had a curious encounter in the hallway when I arrived this morning. A total stranger was walking about without any identification. He was a short, tubby man with a bald head, a foreign-looking moustache and a shifty look. Being in compliance, I'm specially alert to possible threats, so I accosted him.

"Can I help you?" I asked, in a polite but firm way. "No thank you," he replied in a thick accent. I persisted. "May I ask what business you have here?" He looked around uncertainly. "I'm looking for Mr Gershon."

My suspicions were immediately aroused. Here was a person who fitted a potentially dangerous profile seeking out our chief executive. "Perhaps you'd better come with me," I said taking his arm, intending to lead him down to Security. "No, no!" he resisted. We got into a bit of a tussle, when suddenly Gershon's office door flew open and my boss stepped out. "My dear friend!" he cried. "Welcome to my humble abode!"

Least said, soonest mended. I beat a hasty retreat, but made a mental note to send a memo to Security. All visitors MUST wear badges and be accompanied AT ALL TIMES, specially those who appear to belong to HIGH-RISK ETHNIC GROUPS.

Gershon called me in later. "My visitor was very nice about it," he said with a glower. "But I must ask you to treat important customers with more tact." I remained silent. I had done nothing I need apologise for.

Wed 24 Oct: Got an "expert investor" application in this morning. It was from a Russian gentleman called Beszubov who said he was about to settle in London, having made his fortune in oil and gas in Siberia. He enclosed reams of bank statements, all in Russian and all, I supposed, in roubles. Anyway, there were lots of noughts, and Rs and Ns written backwards. These were accompanied by a long letter, also in Russian, which I took to be a bank reference.

How could I possibly approve such an application when he hadn't even taken the trouble to present his case in English? Anyway, I called up our records department to see if they had any information about Mr Beszubov. Answer no. I Googled him. That produced a news story about our friend having set up a company called Beszubovneftygaz somewhere up in the Arctic Circle. Unlike other less fortunate Russian oil companies which have been forcibly taken over, his had survived, which made me very suspicious. Russian Mafia, definitely.

I decided to turn the application down, and drafted a rejection letter to Mr Beszubov's address in Chelsea.

Thurs 25 Oct: Had another ding-dong with Security over visitor passes. It appears that the clips that they use to attach the passes to visitors' lapels are not strong enough, and they frequently drop off. I ask you. We spend millions of pounds a year on security and we can't even provide secure lapel badges. I found a website called secure-labelbadges.com, and told Security to get on to them – FAST! I can be quite domineering when aroused…

Fri 26 Oct: *10am*. I gave Security a superior look as I passed through the hall this morning. They really should pull their socks up.

2pm. Horrors oh horrors! I can't speak. I'm going home…

6pm. I'be had sveral big4 whiskies, and I can hardly ty7pe. Had every strip torn off me by Gershon. Beszubovb the foreign gentlemaNn IN THE Hall, Gershon's oldwest friend, will never speak to us again…

Parquet

Gershon blogs:

Mon 22 Oct: Credit markets are paralysed. Prime banks pay a full per cent and more above official rates. Anyone without an entirely lobotomised retail deposit base is bravely whistling in the dark (the Germans say "singing in the woods" – so much better), hoping this is all temporary. Our traders are in deep shock, our computer models in tatters, or the digital equivalent. All in all this is the closest I've been to an organisation which just might not make it.

Tues 23 Oct: All this makes for a particularly taxing backdrop to a long-scheduled meeting with Boris Beszubov, someone who would most certainly qualify as an alpha client. Well connected in the former Soviet Union in both government and commercial sectors (a prize awaits anyone who can spot the difference), he emerged from the Yeltsin era impossibly rich and with half the natural resources of the eastern provinces under his belt.

The only man known to have put on weight in a labour camp, Boris wields a lot of clout. Wondering how to deal with what has been some rather unfavourable press coverage for the bank and which I'm sure he will have seen, I become aware of a scuffle outside my office. I open the door to see Parquet apparently trying to arrest him. I can't even be bothered to ask why. There really are no limits to the man's imbecility.

Wed 24 Oct: I bump into Pauline (easily done) on the way to the monthly Human Resources meeting. She hopes I had a nice weekend (crisis? what crisis?). She has been to stay with her sister and brother-in-law who live on the south coast. Apparently it's very nice and Hastings is very historic even if Lionel the brother-in-law in question doesn't really appreciate it. Sadly, the meeting is due to start before I can absorb any more vital information. Does anyone keep track of her endless days off?

Bridget, our head of HR, has produced *Respect at work 2007*, the sequel to the international bestseller *Respect at work 2006*. There is a much expanded section on the bank's policy on discrimination – including how to treat the fat. I think of making a comment but catch her eye and think better of it. At this rate AFFE will be out of business by the end of the year and there won't be any work, respectful, fattist or otherwise. What planet are these people on?

Thurs 25 Oct: Coming back into the building after a thoroughly sobering meeting at the Bank of England I am accosted by our security supremo Antonio "Tony" Imbroglio. He is in a thoroughly agitated state. Something about Parquet and security passes. The novelty of seeing the world's laziest man doing anything other than just sitting staring into space is of transitory interest. Frankly, I have zero interest in his problems. He and Parquet deserve each other.

Fri 26 Oct: I was very pleased with how the meeting with Beszubov went and when his call is put through I'm in the early flush of self-congratulation. Signing him up as a client would be a chink of light in what has been a grisly month. It was not to be. Not content with asking a whole lot of impertinent questions about where his money came from, Parquet has turned down his application on the basis of his "inadequate financial expertise".

Boris is not happy. I will kill Parquet – or on second thoughts, perhaps Beszubov or one of his mates in the security services would like to do it, since they have so much more experience. A single bullet to the back of the head and an unmarked grave in the frozen tundra. Here's hoping.
Gershon

Superfund

Parquet blogs:

Mon 26 Nov: Well! Phew! What a year that was! Won't we all be glad when it's Christmas!

I don't think I can remember a time when we were under so much stress, worrying about the bank and whether we'd come through OK. Looking back over my blog I see there were several days when I had to stay at the office beyond 5.30pm, even put in time at weekends. I also counted up all the special staff meetings we had to organise: 23! I tell you, Compliance has been working its socks off!

But as I said, it seems to have turned out right: MiFID is now in place and we can relax.

Looking up at AFFE's compliance manual on the shelf above my desk, I can't resist the tiniest feeling of pride not just at its impressive size, but at the quality of the chapter on MiFID, all written (by yours truly) with the greatest clarity – even style! Doesn't someone offer a prize for Plain English? Perhaps there should be one for the Best Compliance Manual. Now there's an idea!

I've sent a memo to Gershon recommending a special bonus for the Compliance Department. I know he's always very sniffy about Compliance: he can't see the point. But for once I think we deserve recognition. Just imagine what a mess AFFE would be in if we'd c***** up!

Tues 27 Nov: *11am.* I've been mulling over my idea for a Best Compliance Manual prize. Who would we get to sponsor it? One of the dozens of consultancies who ring me up every day trying to flog their services. There's an idea.

Gershon wants to see me at noon – to discuss the bonus I expect!

1pm. Sometimes I wonder why I bother. It wasn't about the bonus but some "superfund" he wants to set up to help the bank through all this

market turmoil we've been having. To be honest I didn't fully understand what he was talking about, but he says it will save the bank. He
wants me to get a view from the FSA.

I asked him, what about my memo on bonuses? Gershon immediately
went into one of his rages and almost physically threw me out of his
office and caused me to scatter all my files over the floor. The incident
was witnessed by several members of the Compliance Department. No
one can accuse me of not trying.

Wed 28 Nov: I boned up on superfunds. It seems that American banks
have had the bright idea of putting all their bad debts in a special fund
to get them off the balance sheet and solve the crisis. But I also noticed
that Warren Buffett thinks they're a bad idea, and whatever Warren Buffett thinks, I think too. He's the funniest man I know. Buffett says: "You
can't turn a toad into a prince by repackaging it!" I laughed so much.
Prince. Chuck Prince. Gettit?!!

Anyway I rang up my contact at the FSA. She said they would look
very carefully at the way we valued the loans that were put into the fund
to make sure they were realistically priced. She warned: "This cannot
be a cover for write-offs." I think I got the message. Anyway, I told her
my joke about Prince, and she thought it was very funny.

Thurs 29 Nov: I've been very busy all day drafting a report for Gershon about superfunds. Basically I'm saying they're a bad idea because
they don't actually solve anything unless you can reduce the value of
the assets without writing them down. Which you can't! Or at least, as
Senior Compliance Officer at AFFE, I won't let you!

I had to control my desire to wreak revenge on Gershon for his treatment of me. But I knew I was in a position of power, and he'd need
my consent. I finished my report with the words: "The valuation of the
superfund would have to comply fully with the latest regulations, for

which the Compliance Department is ultimately responsible." I sent the report off to Gershon and went home with feelings of glee.

Fri 30 Nov: Today is Churchill's birthday. I always remember that. How appropriate for my clash with Gershon! He wants to see me at noon.

1pm. A changed man! Gershon invited me to sit down and complimented me on my report – particularly its stylistic clarity. "I wish everyone at AFFE wrote reports that are as good as this," he said. I almost felt warmly towards the man.

Gershon continued: "There's only one problem, and that's how we write down the value of these assets without taking a hit in the P&L."

I replied: "I know. But as I'm sure you understand, it's my job to enforce the regulations."

Gershon looked thoughtful for a moment. "Shall we discuss your memo about a bonus?" I settled more comfortably into my chair.

I shall put it about that I want a copy of Warren Buffett's sayings for Christmas.

Parquet

Gershon blogs:

Mon 26 Nov: Awoke this morning from a most disturbing dream. I was descending the stairs in a sort of multi-storey car park – rather reminiscent of the outrageously priced "Short-term parking" at Heathrow.

When I got to the third level I was confronted by a closed door. I was aware that behind that door lay the most inconceivable terrors. As I waited, a drunken half-witted badger appeared at my elbow – even in this strangely revealing disguise I instantly recognised Gordon Blewitt from GRU Associates, the leading accountancy and audit practice. I wanted to plead with him not to open the door but found myself power-less to speak. As the door swung open a towering panic overwhelmed me and I woke up. What can it mean?

Tues 27 Nov: There is no week so vile that it cannot be made even worse by a long pointless and frustrating meeting with compliance and when I pick up the phone to be greeted by the chipper tones of Parquet, I know that this is to be one of those weeks. Still, we will likely need his co-operation between now and year-end so I resign myself.

In a year when the world financial system has skirted the abyss and in which we have had the first run on a British bank since the nineteenth century, as far as AFFE is concerned you can forget bonuses and count yourself lucky to keep your job. Parquet has come to discuss "a some-what sensitive matter". To start with, I think he is going to resign and I can hardly keep the broad grin of pleasure off my face, but it tran-spires that he has come to demand a special bonus for the Compliance Department. Calmly but tersely, I ask him to leave my office and never to come back.

Wed 28 Nov: Arrived at the office from a breakfast meeting with the lawyers about the treatment of tier 3 ("hard to value") assets. Much emphasis was put on the responsibilities of the audit committee and the application of Sarbanes-Oxley, including the new streamlined "war on terror"-style extradition procedures. Sobering stuff.

What a different scene greets me at AFFE's world headquarters. Antonio "Tony" Imbroglio, our self-styled "Head of Global Security", is sitting at the front desk staring mindlessly into space, not a hair out of place on his exquisite bouffant coiffure and looking for all the world like a study for "Man with no worries".

Getting out on the fourth floor I pass the "Compliance Area" as it is now known. The pink and supremely comfortable figure of Pauline is cosying up to a bun. AP, of course, is nowhere to be seen.

In the next office John Sutton is busy practising throwing balls of paper into his bin. He waves. His new secretary, whose name I forget, is arranging cards featuring inane rabbits around her desk. Perhaps it's her birthday.

Thurs 29 Nov: After Tuesday's gruelling encounter it sticks in the throat to reopen diplomatic relations, but there's no getting around it; the "super SIV" may prove not to be that airworthy anyway, but if Compliance are busy sabotaging the engines it has no chance. I invite Parquet to a meeting in my conference room.

Fri 30 Nov: *1pm.* I am as nice as nice can be. Meanwhile I picture informing Parquet that prior to being hanged, drawn and quartered he will be whipped at the tail of a cart from the City to Tyburn. "I hope that meets your expectations of a special bonus," I tell him as the hangman seizes his scrawny body. Back to reality. It's horrible but I do need his co-operation if we have any chance of making it. Survival is at issue – revenge will have to wait.

Gershon

~

3

Looking for fresh capital

January 2008 began with the biggest falls in stock markets since the dotcom collapse. The Federal Reserve Bank cut interest rates by 0.75%, the biggest single cut in 25 years signalling increasing official concern about the financial system. Stock markets rallied strongly the next day, but it was not to last. MBIA, the US credit insurer and an important link in the game of "pass the risk", announced losses of $2.3bn. In France, rogue trader Jérôme Kerviel added to Société Générale's woes by losing $10bn on "unauthorised" derivative trades.

A previous winner of a prize for "best risk management" the bank showed no inclination to return the award.

The extremely interlinked nature of the financial system was slowly becoming apparent, but the full extent of the interdependencies would not become obvious until after the failure of Lehman Brothers later in the year.

~

Hard to value assets

Parquet blogs:

Mon 7 Jan 2008: Back from my Xmas break. Sixteen blissful days. Acres of time to myself. Redecorated the bathroom AND the caravan! Even managed to read MiFID from end to end. I bet I'm the only person in the City who's done that!

The festivities were marred only by an anonymous gift that came through the post: a book called *The little black book of red tape*, a supposedly funny collection of bureaucratic nightmares done up in a cover that made it look like a packet of regulations. It contained a Christmas card signed "An admirer". Very ha ha. Just the sort of thing clever-Dicks send to Compliance Officers to wind them up.

I've got a sense of humour, but there are limits. The red tape we have here is nothing to do with me: I'm only doing my job, implementing the torrents of stuff that come from the regulators and the auditors. And to prove it, I've made a New Year resolution: to slash red tape at AFFE. Starting tomorrow!

Tues 8 Jan: I was getting down to my anti-red tape campaign when Bridget Brace, head of HR, dropped by with a cross look on her face.

It appeared, she said, that many AFFE employees took unauthorised days off over the Christmas period. What's more, they managed to conceal the fact by creating a virtual presence for themselves on the computer system. Unless you actually walked by their empty desks, you'd think they were in the building. This must be stopped, she said, and stormed off down the hall.

Not my problem, I thought – for once!

My campaign needs a catchy name. What about ART, for Anti Red Tape? That's short and sharp – and rather sophisticated.

It also needs a crystal clear objective that everyone can buy into.

I propose that we eliminate TEN PER CENT of the rules in the compliance manual, just for starters. And once ART gets going, we'll push that number up – relentlessly. We must stretch if we're going to win.

My next task is to create procedures to achieve this objective. I'll put together a blueprint tomorrow.

Wed 9 Jan: I'm working on the blueprint. First, we need a steering committee. This will have to consist of the top people in the bank to give it clout.

I'll ask Gershon to head it. Under him we'll have all the department heads and me driving it forward. Each month, we'll review progress and set fresh targets.

But it's not just a matter of cutting EXISTING RULES. We must stop the flow of NEW RULES.

I propose that we also introduce procedures to assess all new rules to see whether we really need them. This will be done by a Regulatory Impact Committee. I'm sure Gershon will want to head that one, too: he gets real pleasure from squashing regulators.

All this will be backed by a high-profile internal publicity campaign with a catchy slogan. What about "CUT IT OUT! Get rid of those red tape blues". I can feel my imagination beginning to flow. If it works, AFFE could even become a model for other banks in the City. I could become famous as the man who finally reversed the regulatory tide.

I'll need a little secretariat to run the committees and manage the publicity campaign, two or three people maybe. And a small budget, around £100,000. But just think of the money we'll save!

I've put all this into a report that I'll present to Gershon tomorrow. He'll be delighted, I'm sure.

Thurs 10 Jan: Went in to see Gershon this morning and found him with Bridget reading a report. He was scowling. He looked up at me.

"Ah, Parquet. This is very disturbing. Bridget informs me we have malingerers here. People who are not putting in their hours, people who have learnt to subvert our systems and skive off."

He slammed the desk. "I'm not having that! Not with the ridiculous salaries we pay these people. I want you and Bridget to beef up our attendance rules and circulate them to every member of the staff – hard copy – with a warning from me that breaches will not be tolerated. Do you hear? Now go!" He glared at me as if it was all my fault.

I wanted to tell him about my ART initiative but realised that this was not the moment. So I placed my report on his desk and allowed myself to be dragged out of the room by Bridget.

Spent a miserable afternoon adding new clauses to the attendance rules and printing out 2,500 copies.

Fri 11 Jan: Gershon called me in. He was reading my report. "Good idea Parquet," he said. "But bad timing. The only way to make these

shirkers work is by throwing the rule book at them, so I want it to be heavy." A wave of relief flowed over me. "No problem," I replied.
Parquet

Gershon blogs:

Mon 7 Jan: Return to Subprime Hell. Memories of celebrating the sanctity of family life – the lighted Christmas tree, firelight shining off the uplifted faces of our angelic children – are already swamped by anecdotes from the company's Christmas party.

Highlight: an unnamed damsel from client services was forced to abandon her underwear after a mysterious accident (how this became general knowledge is a greater mystery still). *Highlight:* the well-oiled girlfriend of one of our junior traders nearly came to blows with Bridget (she of *Respect at Work 2007* fame). *Highlight:* Kevin from accounts caught the last train home to Kent only to remember that he had moved to Sussex. That's it – no sordid subsidised bacchanal next year; there must be health and safety reasons galore to ban it.

Tues 8 Jan: This is already Wall Street's worst start to the New Year since 1931 – not that you would know it looking around here. Very much business as usual. Tony "Head of Security" Imbroglio has re-turned from two weeks visiting his family in Italy. I refrain from ask-ing who has been prosecuting the War on Terror in his absence. Most of the girls in the office seem still to inhabit fluffy-bunny heaven; even our CFO seems to be struggling to make the connection between global financial meltdown and the rapidly ebbing fortunes of AFFE. Only Bridget seems to have begun the New Year with a grim sense of purpose. What it is we shall doubtless all discover soon. She is not a happy girl.

Wed 9 Jan: I didn't have long to wait. Bridget is waiting for me as I return from Finance Committee. While the rest of us have been attending Midnight Mass, listening for sleigh bells etc, she has been working on a plan to identify malingerers and bring them to justice. Where, I wonder, would the totalitarian regimes of the world be without the Bridgets to run them? It seems, from what she says, that malingering and unauthorised absences were rife over the Christmas period. I manage to maintain an expression of amazed incredulity – what extraordinary revelation is coming next?

Thurs 10 Jan: It is a fact universally acknowledged that there is no problem that an initiative from Parquet cannot make worse. Sure enough my New Year introduction to our Head of Compliance ("Compliance – the nerve centre of AFFE" as he once memorably described it) comes with the familiarly loathsome figure entering my office with what looks unpleasantly like an initiative in his hand. Fortunately Bridget is setting out her plan for the liquidation of the kulaks and clearly something in her expression sends him scuttling for cover, leaving behind an enormous file.

Fri 11 Jan: Parquet's leavings prove to consist of a massive tome, catchily entitled ART (Anti Red Tape. Geddit? – you couldn't make this stuff up.) Never mind. At this rate our sufferings will soon be over. The audit of our trading book begins next week. Tier-three "hard to value assets" and plenty of them. No such problem in putting a price on our personnel. Zero sounds good to me.
Gershon

~

In February, the G7 raised its estimate of system-wide losses from subprime mortgage lending to $400bn. This potentially left many banks short of capital and the search was on to find new backers. The exporting nations of the Far East had built up enormous reserves; essentially their accumulated profits from selling goods to the West. The oil exporting nations were in a similar position and both were eagerly courted. Some succumbed, to their temporary, if not to their permanent regret. AFFE's Gershon joined the hopeful exodus to the Treasure Islands of the Orient.

~

A voyage to Treasure Island

Parquet blogs:

Mon 25 Feb: I'm extremely pleased with the "WALK DON'T RUN!" signs that I've had put up in all the hallways and corridors. Apart from preventing a recurrence of the nasty collision between Bridget Brace, the head of HR, and a panicking derivative trader, it sets a tone that is very in tune with the times – I think. We must all keep calm.

Having said that, though, I'm all of a jitter this morning. I woke up from a dream in which Jérôme Kerviel was plotting to destroy AFFE. He had the keys to every office in the building and was going to smash the Compliance Department computers when I screamed… all my worst fears in one nightmare.

But it doesn't do for compliance personnel to seem anxious. I must inspire confidence, walk tall, radiate tranquillity. Keep up the share price.

Tues 26 Feb: *10am.* Gershon wants to see me at noon, probably to discuss confidence-building measures. I must have a few ready. What about a rogue trader alert, a briefing on the Tripartite Arrangement and a daily update on our successes in subprime exposure management? All these would be very interesting and would give staff the feeling that management was on top of things.

1pm. Very curious. Gershon didn't want to talk about compliance at all. He told me that he was exhausted by recent events and needed to take a few days' holiday. He was counting on me to help the rest of management to maintain order in the bank. "I don't want any nasty surprises," he said. And with that he was off.

What a moment to choose! The markets going haywire, the FSA and the Bank of England in chaos. And suddenly the boss says he needs a rest. I've often thought that Gershon was not up to the job, and now I'm sure. But this is my chance to show my mettle.

Wed 27 Feb: All quiet. I did my "walking tall" act around the building. I noticed that some of my WALK DON'T RUN! signs had been ripped down. I ordered them to be put back. I also had the idea to put up pictures of Kerviel, half as a joke but also half as a warning. The last thing we need is a SocGen at AFFE.

Thurs 28 Feb: A quiet night.

Well I'll be ****!! I happened to glance up at the Bloomberg screen and what did I see!! Gershon hurrying into the lobby of Singapore's largest sovereign wealth fund, pursued by the local media!! He was fending off reporters and cameras with a furious look on his face. "Out of my way!" he was shouting.

When he'd gone inside, the Bloomberg reporter came on the screen. "As you saw, Mr Gershon refused to comment on rumours that he is seeking a $10bn bail-out for AFFE, the troubled European financial conglomerate. AFFE has been among the worst hit by the collapse of the subprime market, and is now running cap in hand to Singapore for a life-saving injection of funds from the Singapore government. The condition of the bank is obviously much worse than people think. We will bring you more news just as soon as we get it."

All hell broke loose in the AFFE building. People started running and shouting, phones ringing, e-mails pouring in… I could see AFFE's share price nose-diving on the trading screen. I was so stunned I could hardly move. But I knew what I needed to do: get out there and calm people down. The trouble was I hadn't a clue what was going on. My phone rang. It was the head of trading. "What the hell's Gershon up to?" he roared. I put on my calmest manner. "All will be revealed," I replied, and fled for home.

Fri 29 Feb: What a night! The phone never stopped ringing: the media, colleagues, the regulators. And when it wasn't ringing I was desperately on the line to Singapore trying to track down Gershon, who seemed to have vanished into thin air. Even his PA couldn't locate him. It was all over the TV news. I managed to snatch a few minutes' sleep but that Kerviel nightmare kept coming back.

When I got into the office this morning, all was strangely quiet. Had we finally gone bust?

I switched on Bloomberg, fearing the worst… But there was Gershon, all smiles in a TV studio. He was saying: "…which will help rebuild our capital and make a new start. I'm obviously grateful to Singapore for their support, but I think they'll find they've made an excellent investment."

I "walked tall" round the building again, making a mental note to draft new rules on internal communications: Gershon is obviously quite hopeless in that department. If it wasn't for AFFE needing my confidence-inspiring presence, I'd take a few days' holiday myself.
Parquet

Gershon blogs:

Mon 25 Feb: It seems only hours since the repulsive Christmas decorations were taken down from the office and already something equally inane has taken their place. Every available piece of wall space has been filled with a notice saying "Walk Don't Run!"

My first thought is that this is a Human Resources Health and Safety Production orchestrated by Obergruppenführer Bridget. Upon more mature consideration of the artwork, I revise my opinion. The author has obviously recently completed a child's guide to PowerPoint course; the jolly colours and that exclamation mark (!) hardly convey that sense of totalitarian threat that Human Resources usually contrives. Obviously the work of a halfwit, not that this narrows the field much – a good 80 per cent of the bank's employees are firmly in the frame.

Tues 26 Feb: While most of AFFE's staff occupy themselves with on-line shopping, texting their friends and celebrating each other's birthdays, there are arguably more pressing issues at hand. The fact is that a major injection of new capital to strengthen the bank's competitive position and to enable us to, ahem, take advantage of exceptional opportunities thrown up (now that's an apposite metaphor) by the current turmoil, would be timely. Very timely indeed, actually. To this end, a visit to the legendary treasure caves of the mysterious Orient has been planned. Yes – it's cap in hand to the Singaporeans.

If I tell our CFO where I'm going, John will insist on knowing every detail and within half an hour the whole street will know – Blunt Northerner in manner, incontinent sieve by nature. No, this is a mission for our chief compliance officer. Parquet's total lack of imagination makes him the ideal man. He can hold the fort. (Such a reassuring image when the Jérôme Kerviels are invariably inside the stockade.) He seems quite nonplussed when I advise him of his new responsibilities.

Wed 27 Feb: At the airport I'm delighted to see that the "war on terror" is being fearlessly prosecuted by our brave boys and girls as my shoes are removed and my hand luggage rummaged through. In front of me another passenger who also fits the profile of an Islamic suicide bomber has also been pulled over. It must have been the Chelsea Pensioners' uniform that alerted the security staff. The relative tranquillity of seat 3A is a welcome relief.

Thurs 28 Feb: Filling in my landing card for Singapore. "Drug smuggling carries the death penalty," it says at the bottom. The economy of the message is very pleasing; no need for lengthy explanations.

Car to my hotel for a quick shower and then on to The Meeting. The steps of the new office building in Robinson Road are crawling with reptiles including the now ubiquitous Bloomberg – they can smell blood. It's hard not to feel excitement as well as dread.

Fri 29 Feb: Twelve hours ago the last people on the planet I wanted

to see were the ladies and gentlemen of the press. What a difference a day makes – the Bloomberg studio couldn't seem more welcoming, the girls beautiful, the soda ice cold. I could hug the interviewer. Lights, camera, action.

"Would you like to comment on reports that AFFE has taken large losses on its credit derivatives portfolio?" Relaxed smile, expansive gesture – top hat on table, tap of the wand and abracadabra – wait for it – enormous, bloated, furry, multibillion dollar Singaporean rabbit.

Thank you ladies and gentlemen, you've been a wonderful audience. I'm Edward Gershon. I'll be here till Saturday.

Gershon

~

By March 2008 the crisis had started hotting up. Bear Stearns was acquired by JP Morgan in a deal brokered by the authorities and backed by $30bn in Fed loans – even so, some semblance of a commercial transaction was preserved. Over the next two months Royal Bank of Scotland would raise $12bn in the biggest capital raising in UK corporate history and Union Bank of Switzerland would announce $37bn in losses on US mortgages. It still appeared to many that this was a serious but localised financial problem. The world economy was still growing and commodity prices soaring. In fact, amidst much clamour about a "commodity super cycle", oil prices did not reach their peak until July.

~

Easter break

Parquet blogs:

Easter Mon 24 Mar: I don't know why people bother to go away over Easter.

The news on television has been full (as usual) of scenes of chaos at Heathrow while I have been quietly tending my daffodils and soaking up the early spring sunshine.

Deirdre is hanging new curtains in the caravan (we've decided it's going to be the battlefields of the Somme this year).

Actually, I've had a bright idea. Why doesn't the government stagger bank holidays? Surnames A to L would be allocated one weekend, M to Z the next. Just think of the chaos you'd save, the sanity you'd spread. I think I'll have another Woodpecker.

Tues 25 Mar: Back at the office. The newspapers are full of stories about the next stage of the Northern Rock disaster. What a total mess this government has made of its financial policies! The first bank run in 100 years, relations with the FSA and the Bank of England in tatters, the capital gains tax fiasco, the non-dom tax thing.

It just goes on and on. The chairman of the CBI said it looked as if policy was made on the back of a fag packet, and I couldn't agree more.

Which reminds me. The Treasury has asked for feedback on its new proposals for financial reform. This is our chance to help put things right. I must draft a paper and get Gershon to sign it. Actually, I've noticed an unnatural air of calm about the place, which must mean he's not around. Maybe Heathrow's super new Terminal 5 lost his baggage (snigger).

Wed 26 Mar: I have to take some of yesterday's words back. I've been through the Treasury proposals in detail, and they're quite good.

The section on how to stop banks failing is specially well thought out: better risk management, a stronger regulatory framework and, of course, a much bigger role for Compliance. In fact it looks as if the Compliance Function is to be upgraded all round, specially in a crisis: hotlines through to the FSA and all that sort of thing

This is only sensible, of course, because the Compliance Department is the only section of the bank that is able to take a complete and objective view of the bank's affairs.

I'll write up a generally positive report, but just pick a few holes for form's sake. Can't let the Treasury think they got it all right!!

Thurs 27 Mar: Gershon is back, I can tell from the loud voices down the hall and the whiff of stale cigar smoke.

His delayed return is apparently because he got bitten on the foot by a snake during his Easter getaway in Crete. At least that's what his PA told me when I went round to book a meeting with him tomorrow morning.

I've finished off my report now, and I'm quite pleased with the result. It analyses each proposal in authoritative detail, listing the pluses and minuses, all wrapped up in a cool but constructive tone. Lots of appendices and references. Just the sort of thing a thoroughly professional Compliance Officer should produce. All it needs is a snappy title. How about "Getting it right for a change"? That's so full of puns and innuendo I can hardly believe I dreamt it up.

The report is slightly longer than I would have liked, about an inch thick. But I've had several copies printed up and comb-bound to make it easier for Gershon to read.

Fri 28 Mar: *10am.* I was astonished on the way in to read a letter in the *Financial Times* suggesting that bank holidays be staggered to get rid of travel chaos. So I am not a lone loony! For some reason the letter-writer added that the new system should be introduced on the first day of April, i.e. next week, which seems a bit soon.

I'm due to see Gershon at 11 am.

12 noon. He was a sorry sight, looking all red and puffed up with a bandaged foot propped up on a chair. There were mountains of unread papers on his desk. He was obviously in a bad mood.

"Well, Parquet, what is it?" he asked.

"I need to talk to you about the Treasury's proposals to reform the UK financial system," I said.

I could see his eyes turn to heaven.

"They're utter crap," he said. "I read them on the plane, and decided the best place for them was at the bottom of a Cretan well. Tell that to the Treasury and put my name on the bottom. Now go."

If working for AFFE does one thing for you, it teaches you to fight despair.

Parquet

Gershon blogs:

Mon 24 Mar: Easter break. Mercifully, here in Crete the howls of financial anguish are somewhat muted. In fact during the frequent Blackberry outages it's almost possible to believe one's on holiday.

Even this limited idyll is brought to a sudden end by being bitten on the foot by one of the local reptiles. Even more unwelcome are the attentions of another representative of the local fauna, the "doctor" produced by the tour company.

Ingratiating and incompetent in equal measure, he dresses the wound with an almost unbelievable lack of basic dexterity before prescribing some filthy medicine, which from the label appears to be an oral contraceptive for goats.

Tues 25 Mar: Vile journey home. Long delays at Heraklion due to "industrial action" by the Greek air traffic controllers in support of a hyper-inflationary pay claim. At Heathrow the usual insolence from the foot soldiers in the "war on terror". It'll be a relief to be back in the office.

Wed 26 Mar: The pleasure of returning to the office is made still greater by receiving a "complimentary" (in what sense is it "complimentary" for heaven's sake?) copy of the UK Treasury's latest taxpayer-funded attempt to whitewash its role in the never-ending sequence of financial debacles.

Masquerading as a series of proposals to "improve" the regulatory regime, I shudder to think how many man-hours Operation Stable Door has already consumed.

Thurs 27 Mar: The trading room seems to have been devastated by a mysterious disease carrying off all males under the age of 30.

It appears that they have departed en masse for Silverstone where they are putting "the world's most desirable cars through their paces", courtesy of one of the investment banks.

Self-caricature doesn't begin to describe it. Two questions come to mind. If these mindless entertainments don't act as an "inducement" why do our brokers bother?

And why is it that however many billions they lose they always seem to have unlimited entertainment budgets?

Fri 28 Mar: Another month, another unwelcome financial innovation. Markit, purveyor of credit indices to the gentry, is proposing a new index allowing hedging of credit exposure to auto loans.

With little appetite to enter a new subprime-style hell, there will doubtless be plenty of people eager to hedge their exposure and relatively few anxious to underwrite it.

Up will go the cost of protection and, when this is front-page news, the accountancy profession will stir from its traditional slumber, suspect something is up (are those the tumbrils of litigation I hear approaching?) and insist that auto loans are marked to market. The resulting avalanche of distress selling will hammer the credit indices and force further write-downs. The term "one-way street" comes to mind. Three cheers for this latest enhancement to the financial Doomsday Machine.

No such worries for Parquet who has requested a meeting. It seems that he has read the Treasury's offering and has found it very much to his taste.

He wonders if I would like to endorse his "reply". I do so wish he would go away.

Could I tempt him with an overseas posting? Would he entertain a prestigious opportunity in the medical field in Crete? It's one of the few things for which he is clearly qualified.

Gershon

Downsizing

Parquet blogs:

Mon 21 Apr: I knew it, I just knew it. After the losses comes the blood-letting.

We got in this morning to find a memo from Gershon announcing that AFFE must "downsize" by 10 per cent to cope with "a crisis of utterly unprecedented proportions". He wants volunteers to take up "an exceedingly generous exit package", and if there aren't enough "there will regrettably have to be redundancies, though these will also be generously treated".

Tremors are running through the building. I should feel secure – after all, Compliance is the binding that holds a place like this together. But I know that Gershon thinks Compliance is a waste of money, and he may use the downsizing as an excuse to cut our Function back. I must be careful.

Perhaps I should write a memo saying that this is exactly the moment to strengthen Compliance rather than weaken it. All our Control Systems, Audit, Risk Management, Enforcement etc. are absolutely vital to the bank's survival in tough times.

I've had another thought. Why not invite my FSA contact out to lunch to share ideas on the need for more Compliance? What a good idea. I'll call her tomorrow.

Tues 22 Apr: There are rumours that Jack Prime, the head of structured products, is among the first to go. (Jack "Sub" Prime to his friends!!) No surprise there. It's thanks to him that AFFE is lumbered with massive loss-making positions in all those collateralised thingies that nobody understands – and he still got a bonus last year for creating business! What a daft world.

Jack occupies the corner office on our floor, so if he goes, we shall see who the next up-and-comer is in the bank. Corner offices aren't just for anybody.

My FSA friend was delighted to be invited out, only she asked to meet "somewhere discreet". We have a date tomorrow.

I watch a steady stream of people passing down the hall to Gershon's office at 10-minute intervals. This is not a good time to be working in a bank. There's so much gloom about that I shall go home early.

Wed 23 Apr: I arrived at the office to be greeted by a tremendous shouting match going on down the hall in Gershon's office. The door burst open and out stormed the head of corporate finance and the head of asset management, literally at each other's throats. There was hate on both their faces and they were screaming all sorts of blue language at one another.

What a disgraceful display! As Head of Compliance I feel I have a duty to preserve order, so I run over and try to pull them apart. I should have known better. I get a stream of abuse from both of them and a punch in the face. It takes several minutes for them to calm down, and eventually they stalk off in different directions making rude signs at each other.

I poke my nose into Gershon's office. "Can I help?" I ask in the tone of authoritative concern. All I get is another stream of abuse for my pains.

So it was very consoling to have lunch with my FSA friend (I really feel I shouldn't name her in case this blog gets into the wrong hands). Basically she and I are totally on the same wavelength: we're regulatory pals, we share visions, we both want London to be the best-run financial centre in the world.

What she said was very useful. Post-Northern Rock, there's going to be a huge drive to strengthen Compliance and Risk Management, and people like me will become key players in the business. The FSA will shortly be circulating a memo to banks telling them to beef up the whole control side. What wonderful news! All will be well.

Back at the office everything is still buzzing with the morning's fisticuffs. It turns out that they were fighting over Jack Prime's corner office. What pathetic children.

Thurs 24 Apr: I spent most of the morning drafting a memo to Gershon laying out the case for more Compliance, with just a hint that the FSA might shortly be pressing precisely that point. I deliberately keep the tone understated. When you've got strong cards, you don't want to overplay your hand. I dropped it off in Gershon's office before heading home. He looked haggard.

Fri 25 Apr: *9.30am.* The air is still tingling with fear. There is an envelope on my desk addressed PERSONAL. I feel a cold shiver run over me. Maybe I've been deluding myself all along. Inside is a note from Gershon's PA. He wants to see me at 10.40 am for ten minutes.

I can't believe it. After all I've done for the bank. To get the chop. Incredible.

11am. I still can't believe it. I went in to see Gershon at the appointed time. He had my memo in front of him. "Parquet," he said. "I don't usually have good news for you. But I'm expanding your department. And what's more, you can have Jack's corner office."

3pm. I finally pluck up the courage to enter my new abode. I sit at the desk and am overcome by a feeling of utter pleasure.

Parquet

Gershon blogs:

Mon 21 Apr: Even with the multibillion dollar Singaporean rabbit installed in the building and radiating warmth, the temperature is still perceptibly dropping.

I hope another trip to Treasure Island isn't immediately necessary. Filling in the immigration form with what is probably already the new improved warning "Drug smuggling and lack of financial candour carries the death penalty in Singapore," is not a pleasant prospect.

No, it's downsizing time and we'll see just how much difference that makes; most of these people are a waste of space anyway.

Tues 22 Apr: Redundancy day. Time to don the black cap and recite the approved script. Bridget has truly excelled herself this time. "I would also like to take the opportunity to thank you for the extraordinary contribution you have made to the firm's success," (which is why you are being fired with the statutory minimum payout). Even without her black shirted figure smirking malevolently in the corner while ensuring that due process is followed this would sound pretty insincere.

As it is I almost feel sorry for the victims. But what beggars belief is that almost without exception everyone seems utterly amazed at being given the heave-ho.

Surely even *Sun* readers have heard of the global credit crisis by now?

Wed 23 Apr: At least two of my most senior people have decided to show some leadership in these troubled times.

The trading room is treated to the edifying spectacle of two department heads fighting in the corridor – and bloody bad they are at it too. I wonder what they are fighting about.

There again, who cares? A couple of hours counselling by Bridget and they'll be suitably regretful. Parquet pops his head in and offers to help. Help?

Thurs 24 Apr: We all know that there is one business which will benefit from this sorry mess – compliance and regulation. Considering that the subprime mess is largely the consequence of a US government mandated drive for "financial inclusiveness" this result is, shall we say, ironic.

Fri 25 Apr: At least there is some good news; the lease on the floor downstairs is up for renewal in the summer so we will let that lapse and consolidate on the top two floors – it will be a bit of a squash at first but there will probably have to be some more bloodletting later in the year unless there is a miracle upturn.

Parquet is summoned to be told of his new responsibilities. They are not quite as glorious as he probably supposes. I'm assigning some building maintenance functions to compliance – it may be helpful to be able to show the FSA that we are investing in the area.

I also tell him about his new billet – the coveted corner office overlooking the river. Shall I also break the news that he will be sharing it with Pauline, John Sutton and the boy from accounts with the personal hygiene problem? Or shall I leave that until next week?

After all it is Friday, why spoil his weekend?

Gershon

~

The corner office

Parquet blogs:

Mon 19 May: I'm thrilled with my new corner office with fine views across the City. At last Compliance has got the recognition it deserves! I've stuck a notice on the wall saying "THE BUCK STARTS HERE" to remind people that Compliance lies at the heart of every profitable business.

Key lesson from the credit crunch: you can trace every crisis back to someone breaking the rules. I've said so time and again, but it's part of a Compliance Officer's lot that people stop up their ears to glaring truths. How does the song go? "A Compliance Officer's lot is not a happy one."

I see from the newspapers that merger mania is in the air once again. Takeover rumours are swirling around all the big bank groups, including AFFE. But I'm certain after the big refunding we did with the Singapore wealth fund that AFFE is safe. If it wasn't, I'd be the first to know!

Tues 20 May: I was astonished when I got in this morning to find three more desks in my office. I'm told that AFFE is shrinking its space to save money, and we all have to double up – or in my case quadruple up. I have to share with Yorkshireman John Sutton from finance, as well as Pauline my assistant and someone from accounts who I've never seen before.

I was furious. I stormed in to complain to Gershon but found his office full of men in dark suits and tasselled shoes. Gershon waved me away. Why does he waste his time talking to people whose sole purpose in life is to put the bank at risk and then pocket all its profits in bonuses? If he'd spent more time on Compliance we'd never have had to go cap in hand to Singapore.

Wed 21 May: My office has really become impossible. Sutton is never off the phone, gossiping with everybody in sight in his loud northern way. The man from accounts, whose name is Norman, spends the whole time scratching himself and saying nothing. I'm used to Pauline's incessant sweet-eating, but not at such close quarters. How can I possibly ensure that AFFE is a Fully Compliant Bank with all these distractions?

Sutton is a conspiracy theorist. He thinks that we're a target for one of the up-and-coming oil-country banks who want to get into the London market. Imagine! AFFE falling prey to a bank that didn't even exist 10 years ago! What is the world coming to? It simply can't be true. In any case, Compliance would have to be consulted before anything went forward, and I've heard nothing.

Thurs 22 May: The atmosphere in the office is so awful that I have decided to go back to my old cubicle. The trouble is that it is now occupied by TWO of Gershon's PAs. They said he was far too busy to see me. As they spoke, I saw him sweep down to the elevators surrounded by suits and chunky cufflinks. I thought we had got rid of all those types in last month's shake-out.

The rumours continue to swirl about. I got a call from my FSA contact asking what was going on. I told her confidently that there was nothing going on, because if there were, I'd be the first to know. She said "humph" in a tone which I had to take exception to. Who is she to doubt me?

Fri 23 May: I came in deliberately early to get some work done before the rest of the staff drove me mad. One of the first things was to knobble Gershon's PA and get an appointment to complain about working conditions. She said he was up to his ears, and wasn't seeing anyone. I stood tall and said that Compliance was demanding to see him on urgent business.

"I'll see what I can do," she said with a note of impatience that I felt was out of place.

I took a call from the Head of Strategy who wanted to know whether I had any information about the rumours.

"Absolutely not," I said. "And until I get a proper desk, I frankly don't care."

The phone rang again. "Yes," I said with some anger. "Come and see me right now." It was Gershon. I strode into his office with all the dignity I could muster. "I have to complain about the new office arrangements..." I began.

He gave a dismissive wave. "Parquet. I need to inform you as head of Compliance that AFFE is contemplating a merger with Sibgazbank in Moscow which is good for us because it opens up an exciting new market."

I paused to take the news on board. "What does it mean for Compliance?" I asked.

"You will run Compliance for the merged entity, and you will get your office back."

I saw straight away that it was a tremendous deal.

Parquet

Gershon blogs:

Mon 19 May: President's Day in Barakistan. Never a dull moment. Only four months ago it looked as if we might not see the light of another New Year's Day (naturally AFFE now observes the Chinese calendar), but with the installation of the multibillion-dollar Singaporean rabbit (already noticeably trimmer, it must be said) such concerns seemed to recede into the distant past. Now, a new era dawns as, bizarrely, we are increasingly an object of desire for some of the world's newly wealthy financial organisations. Some of these are, shall we say, not exactly household names in the West and could even be described as enjoying the active involvement of some colourful entrepreneurs. However, game old girl that she is, AFFE is looking a little raddled these days and, with another round of write-downs always potentially looming, can't afford to be too fussy.

Tues 20 May: Day of the Revolutionary Peoples in Kamasutrastan. Researching the background of potential suitors is quite an eye opener. For light relief from the rigours of realpolitik (not to say geography, how many – *stans* can there be, for goodness sake?) there is the subject of the office seating plan. I am planning to discover how many people we are able to fit into Parquet's corner office. From a dimly remembered *Guinness Book of Records* entry involving boy scouts and a phone box, the answer is a lot more than you think. We are already up to five, count-ing Pauline as a generous two, and still they come! I'm always on the lookout for new talent. Tony Imbroglio's nephew, Roberto, who works for building services – doubtless he was the best qualified candidate – needs somewhere to rest up between bouts of maintenance. Not only that, but he has what looks like quite a promising skin condition.

Wed 21 May: Heroes Day in Rushdieistan. One thing to be said for the never-ending financial crisis is that it makes the team a lot more bid-dable. No prima donna behaviour. No empty threats to join Goldman Sachs. No preposterous expense claims for suites and in-room massage at the Four Seasons. No loud complaints about "insulting" bonuses. I can see why communism practised constant revolution; it certainly keeps everyone on their toes. I called a conference to let the senior people know what was potentially afoot and they were as quiet as little lambs.

A rather different issue is how the Singaporean mega rabbit will feel about sharing its hutch with a vast ravening wolf from the steppes – but that's for another day.

Thurs 22 May: Day of the Supreme Leader in Ustanistan. Audit Committee; level three assets. Are they worth anything? Who knows? Management accounts; headcount down, expenses up. What to do? Human resources monthly meeting; affirmative action programme update. Are the Irish a minority? Not in Ireland they're not.

Fri 23 May: Natural Resources Day in Nobudistan. Just one last thing to do before the weekend – to tell Parquet that his precious charge is locked in a passionate embrace with a drunken Russian and that if they leave the dance together he is not, repeat not, to attempt to interfere. He doesn't seem to care, lousy chaperone that he is. "What does it mean for compliance?" wheedles the odious creature. "You will run compliance for the merged entity," I reply. What I don't tell him is that in Russia it's never Compliance Day.
Gershon

~

From Russia with love

Parquet blogs:

Mon 23 June: Everyone at AFFE is in a state of great excitement over our proposed merger with Sibgazbank in Moscow, an excitement which I must immediately say that I don't share. I've read enough about Putin and his bully boys to expect nothing but trouble.

Dawn raids, harassment, trumped-up accusations of tax evasion; we're heading for bad, bad times, and Compliance will be in the thick of it. Batten down the hatches I say.

This morning, we all had to sit through a nauseating presentation by Gershon about what a wonderful deal it is. "The next phase of AFFE's growth is about to begin," he proclaimed, and – would you believe it – everybody clapped! Clapped him for selling out to a bunch of – well, I'd better not say... Those Ruskis have probably already infiltrated our computer system and put bugs in all the phones.

Gershon says the merger "will open up new business horizons". But we all know why he really did the deal: to save his skin after we got clobbered in the credit crunch. A true case of "Better Red than dead!"

Thank heaven I'm due for my annual leave next week. I'll be well out of the way.

Tues 24 June: Gershon called me in first thing. "Parquet," he said, "Get your snow shoes on. You're off to Moscow. I want you to team up with Boris Bazookov, your opposite number, and sort out Compliance. Here's your visa. Your flight leaves at 2pm."

"But..." I protested, "I'm going on holiday on Friday." Gershon shrugged. "In that case, I'll put Bazookov in charge of Compliance." I quickly realised that I had no choice.

Later. A nightmare journey. A plane full of drunk Russians and salivating American oilmen, chaos at Sheremetyevo airport, and a taxi driver out of hell. At least my bedroom has a lock on the door, which is just as well since the corridor seems to be the venue for the national vodka finals.

Wed 25 June: Meeting with Boris Bazookov later. Must prepare.

I can imagine him exactly: a ton of Russian meat, with a big black beard and smelly breath. Most likely ex-KGB, put in the bank as the Kremlin's hit-man. Out to destroy AFFE's compliance systems, and strip its assets. I must absolutely be on my guard.

Later. Well, I shouldn't rush to judgment! A chauffeur-driven car delivered me to Sibgazbank's HQ at the top of Gorky Street, which turned out to be a surprisingly elegant modern building where I was courteously received by a charming young lady. She ushered me into a room where there was a young man in a well-tailored suit who spoke perfect English. I assumed this was Bazookov's sidekick. But no. It was Bazookov himself! I couldn't have been more amazed. Maybe Gershon knew what he was doing after all.

Bazookov turned out to be impressively well-versed in the ins and outs of bank Compliance: Basel 2, EU directives, accounting standards and so forth. And we quickly got on like a house on fire. He stressed that Sibgazbank wanted to use the merger with AFFE to achieve "excellence in Compliance" and adopt "best practice" throughout. In no time at all, we were on first-name terms.

I couldn't have been more pleased or relieved. Back at the hotel, I sent a message to Gershon reporting the good news, adding that I saw no problems on the Compliance front.

Thurs 26 June: Boris and I were supposed to have another working meeting this morning. But it all went so smoothly that Boris proposed "a bit of sightseeing" – which I gladly agreed to since this was my first visit to Moscow.

We started with a light lunch of smoked fish, caviar and vodka before touring the sights. Red Square was tremendously impressive: those huge brick walls and turrets, and St Basil's fantastic curlicues in the background. Then through the old Arbat quarter, where Boris insisted that I sample cakes and rose liqueur.

I began slightly to lose sight of things after that, but we ended up in the Café Pushkin where we ate a huge meal with Georgian wines and Armenian cognac and lots of toasts to Anglo-Russian friendship. I don't remember getting back to the hotel. But I must have done since I was there the next morning.

Fri 27 June: Early flight back to London, the head feeling like a Soviet sledgehammer.

Dropped in to see Gershon on the way home to confirm the good news. He looked at me coldly. "Well, they knobbled you, didn't they," he said, waving a photograph of what looked like yours truly propped up by two Russian lovelies, with the message: "We look forward to our close mutual co-operation, Boris".

The swine. Good thing I'm going on holiday or I'd go straight back and thump him with the complete edition of Basel 2.

Parquet

Gershon blogs:

Mon 23 June: Somewhat to my surprise Sibgazbank continues to show interest in getting to know us better. The experience of being courted by a huge bear is, I must admit, a rather unsettling one. I'm not the only one it seems: the Singaporean (ex)-mega rabbit's owner was distinctly unenthused on this morning's conference call. Discussions of new horizons just didn't seem to cut it – it's almost as if it thinks it would be happier cooped up in London than free to roam the steppes with its new friend.

Internally the response couldn't be more different. My presentation to the staff, if not exactly cheered to the rafters was vigorously applauded – any port in a storm, I suppose, even if it is Archangel.

Tues 24 June: Public-domain information on Sibgazbank is hard to find although doubtless there is plenty in the KGB archives. For the first time in his life the wretched Parquet could come in useful. His train spotter's instincts and his total lack of imagination should stand him in good stead on his forthcoming visit to his opposite number in Moscow – incorruptibility comes in different forms.

Wed 25 June: The predictable stream of supplicants trails into my office trying to find out what "The Merger" will mean to them. Why ask me? I don't even know if it's going to happen.

Bridget, our Human Resources head, is quite unconcerned, however.

I assume that she's confident that she won't end up an inmate of the Gulag – she'll be running it.

Thurs 26 June: No word from the loathsome Parquet on how his Russian trip is progressing. Given the thousands of times that an unwelcome communication from the little creep has spoiled my day it's ironic that just about the only time I would like to hear from him there's total silence.

Fri 27 June: I should know by now. When one's dealing with the Parquets of this world there is no level of expectation so low that one can't be disappointed. Boris Bazookov has copied me in on his mementoes of their night out in Moscow – photos of Parquet pie eyed between two hookers. Who'd have thought he even liked girls? I'd have thought gardening was more his line. The air of threat is palpable and we're not (so to speak) even in bed together yet. I'm starting to agree with the Singaporean (ex)-mega rabbit – it can get bloody cold out on the steppe.
Gershon

~

Auditors at the Gate

Parquet blogs:
Mon 25 Aug: Bank Holiday. Back home from our caravan holiday in the battlefields of the Somme. What a dreadful episode of human history that was! As one whose job it is to keep the forces of evil at bay, my heart goes out to all those gallant youths. We all have to make terrible sacrifices.

Tues 26 Aug: First day back at work, and what a sight! The whole bank at a standstill, gripped by fear. What happened to all those gung-ho corporate financiers who only a year ago were threatening to beat me up if I didn't approve their rotten deals? Triple A, asset-backed, hedged to the eyeballs and insured. What could possibly go wrong? I knew better. I insisted on the most rigorous analysis. Fat lot of good. Today, they're all quaking at their desks with nothing to do.

I found a cheery postcard from Boris Bazookov in Moscow. "All your friends send love," he writes, referring to an evening I'd rather forget (though he's gone rather quiet on the merger).

Wed 27 Aug: Gershon calls me in for a post-holiday chat. He is surprisingly genial, and my suspicions are aroused.

"Parquet," he says. "I want you to know that I've asked the auditors to run an inquiry into all that subprime stuff we took on. I want this to be a completely open and honest exercise. We owe it to our regulators, our shareholders, and above all to our staff to lay everything out, exactly as it happened. It's much the best way to rebuild confidence in the bank.

"I hope you will co-operate with them, and bear in mind where your loyalties lie."

Loyalties lie, indeed! When I think back on all the abuse and bullying I took from him last year, my breast boils with lust for revenge.

What Gershon doesn't know is that I have a note of a risk management meeting he chaired where he described the Compliance Function as "a drag on earnings". Talk about a smoking gun!

Thurs 28 Aug: *am.* I had a quiet word with my friends at the FSA. Far from being Gershon's initiative, this inquiry is being conducted at the insistence of the FSA who are curious to know how a bank can lose $10bn and still have the same chief executive six months later.

The FSA is intending to publish the report. Hard to imagine Gershon lasting five seconds.

I have an appointment with the auditors this afternoon.

pm. "The auditors" is a rather grand description for two spotty youths who obviously would not recognise a collateralised mortgage security if it stared them in the face.

They wanted to know how effective the Compliance Function had been. I confronted my dilemma. I could either say it was terrific. Or I could tell them the truth, namely that when it came to it, Compliance was always shoved out of the way in the headlong rush for profits.

I could feel Gershon breathing down my neck. But I remembered those poor lads on the Somme nearly 100 years ago, hurled into the mouths of blazing guns, abused by their superiors, but going over the top for King and Country. That's me, I thought. "You might like to study this," I said, slipping my meeting notes across the table.

Fri 29 Aug: *am.* I really don't know what to expect today. I'm certain I did the right thing yesterday, being true to the integrity of the Compliance Function. I'm the Flanders Trenches, the Thin Red Line, one of The Few standing up for what is right.

pm. I got a call from Gershon about 2pm. I went into his office and found him reading my meeting notes.

"Parquet," he said. "The auditors have asked me to comment on my remarks about the Compliance Function. You realise, of course, that what I said was in jest. No responsible bank executive would ever say such a thing in earnest."

"It didn't seem like it at the time," I replied, recalling that he had snarled in my face as he said it.

"You also realise that if this is published I shall have no option but to resign?" I shrugged and said nothing, though you may imagine my joy at the prospect. He went on: "Alternatively, I could show the auditors the photograph that Boris took of you in Moscow lying drunk in the arms of two hookers."

I very quickly realised that Gershon must indeed have made his remark in jest. As he said, no one in his position could possibly view the Compliance Function with anything but the greatest seriousness.

"I'll just go and have a quick word with the auditors," I said, leaving his office all in a tremble.

Parquet

Gershon blogs:

Mon 25 Aug: Bank Holiday. Even here in rural Sussex the hateful noise of Obamamania penetrates the tranquillity. At least Hank Paulson understands how to treat his friends – let's hope the taxpayer bailout of Wall Street is complete by the time Obama's boys take over. I doubt they'll be so sympathetic.

Tues 26 Aug: Back to the office. The trading room is like a morgue. Corporate finance feels like a wet Sunday in Glamorgan c. 1950. Compliance and Human Resources, however, are humming with busy work. To a large extent this is their dream come true – they can pursue their mission of being an utter nuisance without there being any actual business to get in the way.

With the size of the government help we're going to be looking at we'll soon be a nationalised industry anyway – that should suit the lot of them just fine.

Wed 27 Aug: Even before the taxpayer sees the size of the cheque he's going to be writing for this debacle he's already baying for blood. Even the FSA has heard the distant howls and has started asking a whole lot of damn fool questions. We're supposedly taking the initiative by instigating a thoroughgoing investigation by the auditors. It will reveal precisely nothing of course, but it has two enormous advantages.

1. It demonstrates that we are doing something.

2. While the investigation is under way (this could be a long one) we can't possibly comment on anything until the outcome is known.

Thurs 28 Aug: The auditors are at the gate. I can't stand these people, so they can look forward to many happy hours with Sutton and Parquet. I assume they have the necessary nous to work out that if things weren't done properly it is their fault, ergo they must have been done properly. QED.

Fri 29 Aug: Parquet's total lack of intelligence, common sense and integrity is revealed once again as he imagines he can buy his liberty by handing me over to the acned youths from the accountants. Who does he think pays them? Apparently I subverted his ability to do his job.

A brief interview with the horrid little man sorts it out. As if he wasn't already utterly compromised by working for AFFE there is the little matter of Boris Bazookov's photos of him and the tarts. I never imagined that I would end up finding those photos useful. So now it's blackmail – perhaps I do have the necessary skills to adapt – maybe the public sector won't be so bad after all.

Gershon

4

The mighty humbled

The autumn of 2008 saw the financial crisis move up through the gears. Until then, government intervention had been largely successful. The shareholders in Bear Stearns and Northern Rock had lost heavily, but their other counterparties had emerged intact. This was about to change, and for a while it looked as if the crisis was on a scale too big even for governments to contain. Fannie Mae and Freddie Mac, the US parastatal mortgage giants which had been creaking alarmingly for some time, were taken into government "conservatorship". Never fully of the private sector, they entered another twilight world in which they had become not fully of the public sector. Their role in the housing boom and bust was subjected to little scrutiny and amidst loud calls for greater oversight and tighter regulation of the financial system, an inconvenient truth was overlooked: Fannie and Freddie were already crawling with every kind of Congressional oversight.

Lehman Brothers announced a loss of $3.9bn, failed to find a buyer and filed for bankruptcy. The dominoes started falling fast. Merrill Lynch was bought by Bank of America in a government-sponsored deal. An $85bn rescue package (the eventual total would top $160bn) for AIG was announced. In another shotgun marriage, HBOS joined with Lloyds – a deal which would have been forbidden on competition grounds only a few months earlier. Washington Mutual failed. Dexia, Fortis and Bradford and Bingley were nationalised. The US Congress rejected a $700bn support package for the banking system. Wall Street fell 7% the next day. A week later and after Hank Paulson fell to his knees (sic) to beg for the support of Speaker Nancy Pelosi, an amended version of the bailout bill was passed.

In October, the FSA raised the guarantee on UK bank deposits to £50,000. Germany announced a $68bn bailout of Hypo Real Estate. Iceland nationalised Landsbanki. The UK announced its own £50bn banking bailout package. The Fed cut rates to 1.5%, the Bank of England to 4.5% and the ECB to 3.75%. In Japan, official interest rates had been close to zero for years. Wachovia was rescued by Wells Fargo. After US retail sales fell by 1.25% the Fed cut rates again – this time to 1%. Phew.

~

Management cleared

Parquet blogs:

Mon 22 Sep: We all had to troop down to the conference hall this morning for a pep talk by Gershon, or "McCavity" as he is known in the bank, for his cat-like ability to be elsewhere when disaster strikes.

Gershon looked supremely confident, which is odd for a man who has lost the bank $10bn and should right now be collecting the dole. He was even in shirt sleeves in his efforts to look nonchalant.

Basically his message was that the worst of the credit crunch was past. The bank had been stabilised by his magnificent achievement in bringing new Far Eastern investors on board, and fresh horizons were opening. "Now is the time," he declared, "for an ambitious bank like AFFE to go out there and seize opportunities. 2008 will be a year when AFFE bucks the market and delivers more, not less, profit."

I couldn't believe my ears. From where I sit, the world seems to be falling to pieces. Yet from where he sits, a few yards down the hall, it's all sunshine and roses.

As the person in charge of the bank's Compliance Function, I must ensure that any new business we take on complies with the most rigorous standards. This is not the moment to let up.

Tues 23 Sep: Paul Scheme, head of retail banking, dropped in to tell me his plans to expand mortgage lending in line with Gershon's new directive.

I've heard that bankers have no memory, and that's why they keep repeating the old mistakes. But I thought people were talking about memory loss over a period of many years – "nanoseconds" is more like it.

"We see the housing market bouncing back much sooner than people expect," he said. "The signs are already there. Property prices are levelling out, mortgage rates are coming down – and where's that recession everyone's talking about? If we go out now, we could pick up huge market share."

I felt obliged to inform him that repossessions were at record levels, and the most likely trend in interest rates was UP!!

His eyes glazed over. "Anyway, I just thought I'd let you know our plans," he said, making for the door.

Wed 24 Sep: This is getting boring. Today it was the turn of Vincent Gamboll, the head of investment banking, to tell me his plans.

"You know," he said, his eyes glittering with excitement, "there are deals out there at fire sale prices. If we take them now, AFFE could turn in trillions, TRILLIONS!" When did Gamboll ever care about AFFE? When he talks trillions, it's his bonuses.

Again, I played party pooper. "Vincent," I said, "Brussels is cooking up new regulations that will make it much tougher – and more expensive – to do deals."

"That's the whole point!" exclaimed Gamboll. "We've got to do the deals BEFORE the new regulations come in, i.e. NOW!" He swept out with a parting shot. "You just don't get it Parquet, do you!"

Thurs 25 Sep: *10am*. Gershon has unleashed a whirlwind, and it will destroy AFFE, sure as eggs are eggs. I have to put a stop to it. I've fixed an appointment with him for this afternoon.

4pm. When I walked into his office, he was reading a report. He leant across the desk. "Do you know what this is, Parquet?" Obviously I had no idea, though I could see the name of our auditors on the cover.

"It's the result of the independent inquiry that I commissioned from our auditors last month into the cause of our losses. Would you be interested in its conclusions?" Of course I was.

Gershon continued. "A lot of this is very boring stuff about weaknesses in the Compliance Function which I'll leave you to study. But..." Gershon shuffled a few pages. "Here is the key point. Let me read it to you: 'Management took all necessary precautions against predictable market risk. The fact that those risks assumed uniquely large and unpredictable proportions was not within the control of management.' There, Parquet, what do you think of that?"

I was speechless and left the office in a daze.

Fri 26 Sep: It was all over the *Financial Times* this morning. "AFFE management cleared of recklessness by audit report. CEO launches new growth strategy." Even the newspaper's Lex column managed one of its pathetic puns. "No GAFFE at AFFE."

I have seldom felt more depressed in 20 years in the banking business. Here I am trying to run the Compliance Function in a bank with gung-ho management and auditors who are terrified of losing our business – and the FSA is in a shambles.

I can hear the sound of laughter from the executive suite down the hall. My only consolation will be revenge. Maybe a Deep Throat call to the Sunday newspapers...
Parquet

Gershon blogs:

Mon 22 Sep: If there's no way back, then the only way is forward, as someone or other must have said (Horatius? Napoleon? Mike Milken?). The Singaporean Mega Rabbit (SMR) is now a pale shadow of its former corpulent self and its owner no longer feels that AFFE is a suitable home for any of its brothers and sisters. Boris Bazookov and his mates have become strangely elusive – presumably the pleasures of ethnic cleansing in the Caucasus score more highly on the thrillometer than providing capital to AFFE to seize the myriad new opportunities (more by the day!) in distressed debt. And there's the small problem of a plunging oil price – not that the Russian boom depended on little else. Oh no, not a bit of it.

So, roll up the sleeves, summon the troops and "This is the time for AFFE to go out there and seize opportunities. 2008 will be the year when AFFE bucks the market and delivers more, not less, profit." And pigs might fly.

Tues 23 Sep: Even if our futures all lie in the public sector (£1m a year for running Northern Rock suddenly seems OK) we might as well go down fighting – anyway, what choice is there? That at least is rational. What is not rational is actually to believe our own propaganda. Enter Paul Scheme, head of retail banking, who continues to brim with youthful enthusiasm. Scheme is the stupidest man in AFFE, hotly contested though that prize may be. Even the bouffant Tony Imbroglio, self-styled "Head of Security", has a certain slow, peasant cunning. Scheme is a believer, believing anything, anywhere, any time. Today he surveys the radioactive ash heap that is mortgage lending and sees a broad fertile plain.

Wed 24 Sep: Weekly Investment Banking Review with Vincent Gamboll, who is also full of wide-eyed optimism. What are these people on? To lunch at the Athenaeum with a chap who was in my college and who is now a Very Important Person in the Treasury (VIPITT) and my prospective new best friend. I'm hoping that he won't remember the contempt with which he was habitually treated. Still, all a long time ago and all in good fun, and all that. Rumour has it he's responsible for recommendations such as the Northern Rock sinecure.

Thurs 25 Sep: VIPITT was utterly odious, adopting a most unpleasant air of "We are the masters now". He apparently had perfect recall of every single indignity to which he was subjected at Cambridge including a number that I had quite forgotten myself. My attempts at bonhomie withered on the stoniest ground imaginable.

Better "news" from the auditors' report on AFFE's financial performance during the credit crunch – full exoneration of senior management's
role citing "unprecedented conditions". Some misgivings about the
micro-management of the compliance area, which I must draw to the
attention of Parquet, Pauline and their merry men. Speaking of which,
I haven't seen the lovely Pauline for what seems like weeks – time off
due to stress from overwork, I assume.

Fri 26 Sep: The *FT* is full of the auditors' independent report. "No
GAFFE at AFFE." (Go tell that to the Singaporean (ex-) Mega Rabbit.)

As Darren opens my car door and I'm just about to get in I see the
gaunt figure of VIPITT, an *FT* under his arm, hurrying by. No doubt
he's on some very important official business. He scowls. I smile back.
He always did walk in a funny way.

Gershon

~

Cardboard boxes

Parquet blogs:

Mon 27 Oct: My week has begun extremely well.

First, we put the clocks back yesterday which meant an extra hour
in bed. Not that I need the extra sleep – Compliance Officers are eternally
vigilant (!) – but it gave me time to catch up on my essential reading,
particularly the new UK government proposals to reform financial regulation in the wake of the crisis – all 450 pages!

Second, imagine my satisfaction when I arrived at the office to find another half dozen packages containing more reform proposals from Brussels, the Basel Committee, the Institute of International Finance, the US Treasury, and others too numerous to mention. Some people might balk at all this, but I really can't wait to sink my teeth into them. Fascinating stuff.

Recent events may have struck at the very foundations of international finance, but they have actually given me a huge feeling of – well let's be honest – importance. AFFE has got to be on top of regulatory developments, and I'm the only one who can do it. It's like being in at the creation of the world.

There are so many files that I had to ask Pauline to order a dozen cardboard boxes to store them.

Tues 28 Oct: Unfortunately Pauline messed up and ordered a dozen reams of cardboard boxes, which means we now have stacks of boxes all down the hall. But I laughed to myself and thought: "If new regulations keep coming at the present pace, we'll need every one of them!"

Of course, if banks keep collapsing at the present pace, there may not be many left to regulate. I can't say that I have much time for our management: they're a greedy incompetent bunch. But I will say this for them: they have managed to keep the ship afloat. Maybe they have a secret line into Warren Buffett. If they do, I should know...

Wed 29 Oct: Got an urgent call from Gershon. He was in one of his rages.

"What are you trying to do, Parquet? Ruin the bank all by yourself?"

Given the good work I was doing on the regulatory proposals, I was at a loss to understand what he was on about. "Eh?" I asked.

"All those boxes," he said. "The staff think we're about to shut the bank down, Lehman-style. Out on their ears, clutching their personal belongings. Bridget in HR is working overtime to calm their fears. GET RID OF THOSE BOXES!"

"But," I said, "I need them to store all the new regulatory proposals..."

I won't record what Gershon said, but it was violent and vulgar, and persuaded me to beat a hasty retreat. Spent a messy afternoon stuffing the boxes into the cleaning cupboard.

Thurs 30 Oct: In spite of what Gershon said yesterday, we let another 100 people go today. Although they were all stuck-up corporate finance types, I couldn't help feeling sorry for them: so young and eager-looking. Many were in tears, clutching their boxes and black bags. The office was weirdly quiet after they had gone.

At least they don't fire members of the Compliance Function during a downturn: that would send out quite the wrong message.

I was furious to find that the departed ones had used up their plastic cards to clean out every refreshment machine in the building. Couldn't get a coffee or a bun for love nor money. B******s.

Fri 31 Oct: Spent the morning chewing over the new regulatory proposals with my friends at the trade associations. They're horrified: they see all this as a great regulatory crackdown. That's not how I see it at all: any responsible Compliance Officer must want more regulation, so long as it's good regulation.

Still no buns in the machines. Had to go out to a strangely deserted sandwich bar. Like something from a sci-fi movie after the nuclear holocaust.

I was just leaving for home with some meaty reading matter when the phone rang. It was Gershon. "Parquet, would you drop by please?" I entered his office. He had an uncharacteristic solemn look on his face.

"Do you have any spare boxes?" he asked.

"A few," I replied cautiously.

"Good," he said pointing to a tall pile of files in the corner. "Would you arrange for the secure disposal of those please?"

"What are they?" I asked.

"The personal files of all those who left us yesterday. I don't want to have to think about them any more."

The world's certainly going to be a very different place once this whole crisis is over: lots of familiar names gone, armies of people out of work, whole markets wiped out, complete departments shut down for good. With one exception. The Compliance Function will go from strength to strength. I'm lucky.

Parquet

Gershon blogs:

Mon 27 Oct: I have been troubled by disturbing dreams (invariably waking to a reality far worse than anything my subconscious has conjured). In one, I am a humble supplicant in an oriental palace where a mighty potentate is gracing me with extraordinary largesse.

He smiles benignly as, accompanied by a roll of drums, acolytes present me with an enormous rabbit. I bow. No sooner have I accepted the animal, however, than it starts to shrink. In seconds it is no bigger than a peanut and it scurries away down a crack between the floor-boards. There is a clash of cymbals and the potentate's face turns as black as thunder. Two scimitar-wielding guards tower over me and I awake sweating. What can it mean?

To the office where our very own scimitar-wielding guard, Tony "Head of Security" Imbroglio, displays his usual air of total uncon-cern. Does he have no idea that his employment prospects at AFFE are deteriorating by the minute and that demand for his skills (what-ever those are, exactly) in the world outside is dissipating at an even greater rate?

Tues 28 Oct: The world as we knew it has more or less come to an end. Lehman is bankrupt; Goldman Sachs is now a high-street bank; London house prices have halved; and the stock market has crashed. The economy of the western world has pitched off a cliff. A few brave souls believe that China has a life of its own, but even the embers of this silly fantasy are dying. In the Gulf, the sandy wind whips through the canyons of unsold high-rise condominiums. AFFE survives at the mercy of the ECB while, to the sound of a loudly ticking clock, the Germans make it increasingly clear that they are not going to be picking up anyone else's tab. At AFFE World Headquarters, however, our lives are still governed by immutable ancestral ritual. Today Bridget is presenting the second draft of our New Diversity Policy.

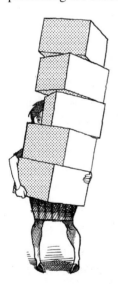

Wed 29 Oct: I go to the office mid-morning after a most vexatious series of meetings at the Treasury and the ("we are the masters now") FSA to find the entire sixth floor full of empty boxes. A tottering pile threatens to collapse on to the mortgage origination desk. Not that it would make any difference – nothing any longer happens there.

A mobile tower stops, wavers, recovers itself to reveal something large, pink and breathless. It is Pauline, our Deputy Compliance Officer. This unwelcome sight confirms what I had already begun to suspect – the boxes must be part of some demonic scheme of Parquet's. His stupidity knows no bounds – of course they will be needed, but you don't need to be a student of *Respect at Work 2008* to know that laying out the body bags ready for the day's fighting is likely to undermine morale. I ring him up and yell at him and, as usual, he sounds slightly perplexed and a bit resentful. I'm really beginning to wonder if any of it makes any difference.

Thurs 30 Oct: 100 body bags today. Familiar routine – briefing senior people on how to break the news – nothing personal, extraordinary circumstances, etc. Usual reaction – shock, surprise, astonishment, hurt, bewilderment, anger. Where have these people been, for goodness sake? Did queues form outside Northern Rock? Did half of Wall Street's investment banks fail? Did the mighty Paulson go on his knees before Nancy Pelosi? Was it somehow possible to have missed entirely the implications for your employment prospects at AFFE? The answer appears to be "yes".

Fri 31 Oct: Apparently there is some use for some of the boxes, though the unnecessarily large number suggests more than usual incompetence in Parquet's area. I'm told he has plans for using them to file all the new regulations. He seems happy. I'd be looking forward to the weekend were it not for the tradition of some new horror being revealed on Sunday night. What will next week's horrid surprise be?
Gershon

~

As November began, the crisis spread. The IMF approved a $16.4bn loan for Ukraine and subsequently a $2.1bn loan for Iceland – the first IMF bailout of a western European country since 1976. The Bank of England cut interest rates to 3% – the lowest level since 1955. Euroland interest rates were cut to 3.25%. A $20bn support package was provided for Citibank after its shares fell 60% in a week. A further $800bn was announced to stabilise the US financial system, $600bn of which was to be used to purchase mortgage backed securities.

In December, the US car industry became embroiled in the crisis. President Bush announced that some of the banking bailout funds would be used to support the automakers. GMAC received $6bn in government support. Bernard Madoff was arrested and charged with an almost unbelievable $50bn fraud. Almost equally hard to believe were the names of the people involved, not only that of "Made-off" himself, but also his associate Ezra Merkin: merkin, a noun, is defined by the Random House Dictionary as "false hair for the female pudenda". In one of the biggest extinctions of savings in history the FTSE stock market index closed down 31.3% on the year, the DAX 40.4% and the CAC 42.7%. Worldwide, real estate prices were falling rapidly.

~

The Christmas Party

Parquet blogs:

Mon 1 Dec: *Christmas is coming, and the geese are getting thin.*
Please put a penny in the banker's tin...

I made that up. It seems far more appropriate to this year's "merrie" season than the old rhyme. After all that we've been through this autumn, AFFE is a mere shadow of its former self. We've shed hundreds of people, there's nothing going on in the trading room.

As I may have said before, the only department that's busy is the Compliance Function. In other words, us! My workload just grows and grows. It's all very satisfying.

Which reminds me – I must keep an eye on plans for the Xmas office party on Friday, which my assistant Pauline is organising. Not that it will be a riot this year: numbers will be small, and I doubt that Gershon will loosen the purse strings – or even show up. But no matter what the size, I must ensure that it complies with the regulations.

Tues 2 Dec: I remember last year, we had a nasty incident when Tony Imbroglio, the head of security, burnt his mouth on a hot mince pie and then banged his head on the door as he rushed for water. There was a lot of blood and Tony was whimpering for a long time, which was really embarrassing (though I noticed that Gershon thought it was all very funny).

I learnt from *Compliance World* (my bible!) that it is now correct procedure to hold a training course for people organising Xmas parties: teach them how to serve hot food, handle drinks, make sure people don't get drunk (and what to do with them if they do!)

Pauline will organise that tomorrow. I've circulated the following message: "AFFE Xmas party. Let's all have fun!! But, please, food and drink may only be served by people who are qualified to do so. To obtain a qualification, you should attend the course in the Compliance Department on Wednesday at 10-12am".

Wed 3 Dec: What a disaster! I should have known better than to entrust the training course to Pauline. The microwave blew up, spattering everyone with scalding bits of Xmas pud. And she used real bottles of wine to demonstrate how to serve drinks, with the result that everyone got sozzled.

Thanks to this cock-up, no one received the proper training. So I've got to scale down. It's going to have to be cold sandwiches and cider. It's the only way we can be sure. I've told Pauline to place the orders – plus some tinsel to liven it up a bit (but nothing that goes bang – far too dangerous).

Thurs 4 Dec: Gershon called me in first thing. He was looking surprisingly jovial given that our business has been chopped off at the knees.

"Parquet," he said. "I've been thinking about the office party. What with the general doom and gloom, I think this will be an excellent opportunity to splash out and jolly everyone up. Let's have the best party ever: champagne, sausages, mince pies, crackers, and maybe even a disco. The works! What do you think?"

"But..." I mumbled, thinking of the orders I had already issued. Gershon cut me off. "Parquet, you're a real wet blanket. I can tell straight away that all you're interested in is the fire regulations. To hell with those. What's more, I want you to dress up as Father Christmas. Don't disappoint me..."

Blast Gershon. I don't really care about all the cider and sandwiches that have been stacked up in the hall. We can dish those out to the poor (i.e. our former employees!!) But I am NOT going to dress up as Father Christmas. If he thinks he can make a fool of the head of the bank's Compliance Function, he's got another thing coming.

Fri 5 Dec: *12 noon.* When I got in this morning, I found a large parcel on my desk. It contained a Father Christmas outfit and a card from Gershon: "Don't disappoint me!"

Word has obviously got out because streams of people came by to make jokes about sledge permits and health and safety for reindeer. Around lunchtime, I thought I would cry off sick. But then I thought: "Dammit! Here's a chance to show that the Compliance Function HAS A SENSE OF HUMOUR!"

4pm. The party starts in an hour. I am off to don my costume.

Midnight. My memory of the party is rather hazy because I (we all) drank rather a lot of champagne, but it seems to have gone quite well. The prospect of seeing the Head of Compliance make a fool of himself was clearly a great draw because crowds of people came. I think I was

even persuaded to get up on a desk and sing "Jingle Bells" after which everyone crowded round me for a boisterous rendering of "For he's a jolly good fellow!" My final memory was of Gershon shaking my hand with a broad grin on his face, though whether it was one of joy or malicious satisfaction I could not tell.

Parquet

Gershon blogs:

Mon 1 Dec: The festive season is off to a roaring start with merrie profit warnings jostling yuletide redundancy announcements for space on front pages.

Nor does my postbag lack seasonal cheer. A nice letter from a senior public official in New York requests details of all employees earning over $250,000. Pointing out the nature of AFFE's new relationship with the taxpayer, he goes on to say that management "must step up to the plate and prevent wasteful expenditures of corporate funds on outsized executive bonuses and other unjustified compensation".

Rather more concise but nevertheless pregnant with understated threat is a Christmas card from a Very Important Person at the Treasury. It says "Season's Greetings" and underneath, in a serial killer's scrawl, "Best wishes, Andrew".

Tues 2 Dec: The fact that the world banking system has collapsed and we are facing the worst recession since the Second World War seems to have no effect on the timeless rituals of corporate life. The dance must go on. Today the dance will be led by the heavy tread of Bridget's boots, for it is the day and the hour for the monthly human resources meeting.

Imagine my joy to discover that we have made "steady progress" towards achieving "challenging inclusiveness targets" – not that this should lull us into any sense of complacency, of course. "Serious challenges still lie ahead" in combating a culture which "while falling short of institutionalised racism and sexism" still fails to meet her standards.

Wed 3 Dec: Walking past the boardroom my senses are assaulted by scenes of wild hilarity. Pauline seems to have assumed the role of a barmaid from a vintage Carry On film: all bosoms, lipstick and coarse laughter.

Various temps (what do we need them for?) are enjoying the full-on attentions of AFFE's young clerical bucks. The place is covered with food and everyone appears to be completely plastered. Everyone, that is, apart from Parquet who is sitting there looking thoroughly disapproving, his mouth puckered like a cat's bottom. He's clearly having a horrible time. If it wasn't for that, I would have closed the bacchanal down and sent everyone home. As it is, I smile and carry on.

A phonecall to the head of the Stasi (aka Bridget) establishes that the debauch was a practice run for the Christmas party. Has the crisis driven everyone insane? Who ever heard of practising a party?

Thurs 4 Dec: After a year of almost inconceivable awfulness – the mass extinction of everyone's savings alone allows it to easily make the grade – there is really no good news except, of course, for our new masters with their index-linked pensions and their burgeoning sense of self-importance. In this hateful environment what could be more appropriate than a lavish Christmas Party presided over by our ghoulish Compliance Officer? I inform Parquet. As usual it is almost impossible to know whether he's pleased, sorry or indifferent. There will be no escape, however, the Santa costume has been ordered.

Fri 5 Dec: The day of the office party has arrived. A time to look back over the triumphs (none) and the disasters (legion) of the past year and to think of employment prospects in the year to come. AFFE is still the front runner. No offers to head a nationalised bank have yet materialised and the FSA is jammed with applications. There is a plan B, however. I shall become a best-selling children's author. The first in the series is called *Chevalier Robert and the Mysterious Secret* and it's very good indeed.

I arrive at the party at 5.30 and the early starters are already well warmed up. Much though I dislike this event it's quite sad to see numbers so thinned out, even if most of them were utterly useless. The girls have made quite an effort I must say. Bridget has put her hair up and after a few drinks looks quite alluring; even Pauline seems to have dropped several dress sizes.

By midnight the scene is positively Hogarthian. Parquet is standing on a desk singing "Jingle Bells". His lamentable rendition is met with rapturous applause. Pauline, clearly in her cups, takes my arm. "I just wanted to say thank you," she says. Thank me for what, for goodness sake?

Yo ho ho and a very merry Christmas to you all.

Gershon

5

Grimm times

In a speech at the beginning of January 2009, President elect Barack Obama described America's economy as "very sick". The Bank of England lowered interest rates to 1.5%: the lowest level in its 315-year history. Angela Merkel unveiled a $67bn stimulus package for the German economy. The ECB cut rates to 2%. Anglo-Irish Bank was nationalised by the Irish government. Bank of America received another $20bn to help absorb losses arising from the purchase of Merrill Lynch.

After a series of late night meetings AFFE received £10bn in government support. James Grimm, a rising star at the Treasury, arrived at AFFE to oversee the UK government's interest in the bank. Citigroup anounced quarterly losses of $8.3bn. Pauline, AFFE's deputy compliance officer, commenced her Carrotplan diet.

The IMF warned that 2009 would see the lowest world economic growth since World War Two with the developed economies experiencing the biggest slump since the 1930s. The following month the Bank of England cut rates to 1% – the fifth interest rate cut since October and US president Barack Obama signed "the most sweeping recovery package in our history": a $787bn economic stimulus plan.

Government bailout

Parquet blogs:

Mon 5 Jan 2009: What a joy to be back at work – and I really mean that. Two weeks of jollity is all very well, but the real pleasure for me lies here: at the heart of AFFE's Compliance Function where I feel I can directly do some good, keeping this show on the road.

I think the Christmas lull has been helpful. The markets are calmer, and AFFE shows a new determination to get through this crisis in one piece. The risk, of course, is that people will start cutting corners, bending the rules to get by. That's where Compliance has to be on the alert!

Which gives me an idea... I shall circulate a memo to all department heads reminding them that "Rules are still Rules!" It will be quite short, about ten pages.

Tues 6 Jan: I get an early call from Gershon. "Would you come in please?"

I go into his office and find him with a copy of my memo in his hands. Maybe he liked it!

"Parquet, what did you do for Christmas?" I explained that we had the in-laws round on Christmas Day and... But he broke in. "Yes, yes, but did you read the newspapers?" I had to confess that I only glanced at the sports pages. "Didn't you read the rumours about AFFE's 'black hole'?" Again, I had to confess that I didn't. But I tried to assert myself: "All quite untrue, of course."

Gershon's face went bright red. "No! That's the point! While you were dallying with your in-laws and circulating useless memos, AFFE is teetering on the brink. This," he said smacking a fat report on his desk, "is the auditors' death warrant. In a sentence, we are in what they call 'a negative equity situation', which for people like you means we're bust!"

Bust! Surely not. The building is still standing, people are coming and going down the hall. I can even hear a telephone ringing in the background. None of that happens if you're bust.

"Yes, bust. Despite all your efforts to ensure that AFFE complies with Basel, MiFID and all the other FSA nonsense, this bank is bust."

I mumbled: "So what are we going to do?"

Gershon leant over the desk. "What every bank does in this situation. It runs in tears to the government, says it's frightfully sorry, and asks for money." He stood up grandly. "We have an appointment at the Treasury 9am tomorrow morning. Unfortunately, you will have to be there."

I stumbled back to my desk, tears welling up in my eyes. Bust! Unbelievable! I slumped against the bookshelf and found my nose pressed against the AFFE Compliance Manual, all 8,500 pages. All that work – for nothing!

Pauline enveloped me in a caring embrace and a gale of perfume. "There, there, Arnold! It can't be that bad!" "But it is!" I cried, and ran out of the building, my life in ruins.

Wed 7 Jan: Up all night, lurching from bewilderment to bitterness to anger and finally to utter exhaustion. I enjoyed a few blissful moments of sleep before the alarm clock rang.

I shook off my fatigue and dragged myself to the Treasury. As I approached the doorway, a large Mercedes drew up and out stepped Gershon and his motley crew. The bank goes bust, but the Merc stays. I ask you.

Our meeting was surprisingly brief, which was good for me since there weren't enough chairs and I had to stand.

The Treasury minister asked: "How much?" and Gershon replied: "£10 billion." The minister went on: "Fine, on the same terms as RBS and Lloyds." Gershon replied: "Done."

I reeled. £10bn! That was more than… I heard Gershon shout "Catch him!" as I fell to the floor. When I came to several hours later, I was lying in the outer office with a lady bathing my face in cool water. Gershon was talking to the minister: "...and I'm really sorry about our compliance man. It really is the weakest part of our bank in every sense."

I was half-carried down to the exit where the Merc was waiting. "Sorry Parquet, only room for three," said Gershon, as they whizzed off and left me on the pavement.

Enough for one day. I struggled home.

Thurs 8 Jan: I called in sick. I really need time to reflect on all of this.

AFFE is bust, the government has bailed it out with £10bn, and we are now owned by the taxpayer. What could be more disastrous, more humiliating – especially for me, the Senior Compliance Officer!

But gradually, I began to see things differently.

Like all Compliance Officers, I am trained to keep calm in a crisis, and that's what I must do. My job is to find the solid ground, to steer the bank towards it, and then rebuild the structure.

In fact, the more I think about it, the more I realise that I, Arnold Parquet, am absolutely central to AFFE's survival. Managements come and go: Gershon and his useless crowd will get the chop, but the Compliance Function will live on. Far from being a disaster, this is an incredible opportunity. I shall design a new strategy for the bank. I shall call it "Growth through Compliance".

Fri 9 Jan: I came into the bank this morning with a jaunty air – very different from all the glum faces I saw around me.

I called Pauline over. She looked tearful. "Cheer up Pauline," I said, "a new life dawns today!"

Parquet

Gershon blogs:

Tues 29 Dec: After an enjoyable day shooting Charlie's pheasants, I am just settling down to lunch when my blackberry rings. It's John our CFO. Apparently we're having difficulty rolling over some of our short term borrowings. A number of questions come to mind. Why are we rolling anything over on 29th December, the most illiquid day of the year? Has John yet to hear of the financial crisis? What does he expect me to do about it? I make a number of terse but constructive suggestions. The line goes dead.

Fri 2 Jan 2009: Against tradition I'm in the office, as is the whole of the senior management group. Looking round the table there is little sign of festive cheer. For the first time John looks as if he's finally woken up to the nightmare that the rest of us have been enjoying for months. He walks us through AFFE's current funding status. Brief synopsis; the Singaporean Mega Rabbit is now so reduced that you need a microscope to see it. The prospect of Sibgazbank kissing our problems better (once an alarming thought, now an unachievable dream) is zero. Our assets are illiquid and increasingly impossible to value. No one wants to deal with us. We need help and we need it now.

Tues 6 Jan: *1.20am.* John and I leave the Treasury with the outline of a deal. Degrading doesn't come close. There's a follow-up meeting on Wednesday to set the official imprimatur on the whole sorry affair. For some unfathomable reason Parquet is required to attend.

7am. After a few hours sleep I'm back in the office. Several hours later, in swans Parquet. I call him in to tell him what's happening – there's not much choice in the matter since his presence tomorrow is "mandatory". From his stunned reaction to the news it seems that the events of the last two years have passed him by in their entirety.

Wed 7 Jan: The day of execution has arrived. We arrive a bit early at Whitehall and sit in the car chatting despondently. We go up the stairs and are shown in. The room is heaving with vulpine, avaricious lawyers and loathsome, condescending officials. What on earth could make it worse? I unwisely ask myself. The answer is not long in coming. For some reason Parquet experiences a fit of the vapours (previously, as far as I know, the sole preserve of a certain type of nineteenth-century heroine) and collapses. While we're all thankful for a bit of light relief, the process of loosening his corset, administering smelling salts etc., drags everything out – something which I, for one, could easily do without.

Finally it's over. Just as we prepare to drive away, an ashen faced Parquet stumbles down the steps onto the street, staggers towards the car and, like some hideous revenant, starts to claw at the window. After all the hard decisions of the last few months it's refreshing to be faced with a really easy one. Without a moment's hesitation I ask Darren to drive on. He floors the accelerator, good lad that he is.

Thurs 8 Jan: We are now a nationalised entity and I celebrate by arriving at the office at the crack of 9.30. Parquet has taken the day off sick, I'm told. Welcome to the new world.
Gershon

A commissar calls

Parquet blogs:

Mon 26 Jan: Now that we've been bailed out to the tune of £10bn by the nation, I feel it's my patriotic duty to clean this place up. What an Augean Stable, a rotting pile of dead and dying so-called assets – we've even got a few million invested in Bernie Madoff's putrefying empire. I've never seen anything like it.

Talk about Herculean tasks. The write-offs in the 2008 accounts will be horrendous. But we have no choice. Armies of accountants are working on it. Fortunately, there are quite a few spare desks to accommodate them.

Tues 27 Jan: "Operation Hercules", as I am calling it, isn't only about cleaning up the past: it's about keeping the stables clean in the future. So we have to make plans to stop new manure.

That means tightening up our lending: no more dodgy mortgages, no more easy overdrafts. We've got to chop back credit cards, call in loans to small businesses which are heading for bust anyway. It's going to be tough, but it's got to be done if we're to stay alive.

And while we're at it, we must prise open our margins: push up loan charges and push down savings rates. I know the Bank of England is cutting interest rates for all it's worth. But that doesn't mean that we should abandon our duty to operate prudently and profitably.

I'm circulating a memo to all our credit officers noting these points. Not that there are many of them left. But in a way, that makes the job easier. The fewer there are, the better I can control them.

Wed 28 Jan: Got in bright and early this morning. Keen to see the effect of my memo. This will be the start of a new era at AFFE, one where prudence prevails.

I had barely stirred sugar in my coffee when the phone rang. It was Gershon. I expected him to congratulate me on my memo, but he was curt: "Parquet, come to my office please."

I entered the room and found him talking to a young man wearing a dark suit and a superior air. "Parquet," he said. "I want you to meet James Grimm. He's from the Treasury, and he's come to look after the government's investment in the bank." I shook his hand.

"He'll be joining us tomorrow, and I've arranged for him to have a desk in your office. I want you to give him your full co-operation."

"Of course," I replied.

I went back to my office, my mind buzzing. What a shock! It had never occurred to me that the government would take that close an interest in us. Gordon Brown said a lot about "not being involved in commercial decisions" in bailed-out banks, and I had assumed we'd be having an arm's length relationship.

But I quickly realised that this was a marvellous opportunity to tell Grimm all about Operation Hercules and get credit for transforming the risk culture of the bank. Yes, this was good news.

Thurs 29 Jan: I made a point of coming in extra early: no good being shown up by a civil servant, even if he is some sort of mandarin! But Grimm was already there with a fat black briefcase and piles of papers.

"Parquet," he said. "As you know, the government has invested a lot of taxpayer's money in this bank, and it's my job to make sure that it is well spent. Later today, I shall be talking to Mr Gershon about AFFE's executive remuneration policies. But in the meantime, I want you to tell me everything about the bank's compliance policies."

I thought the simplest thing was to hand Grimm a copy of my memo. "I circulated this to our credit officers yesterday," I said with a feeling of satisfaction. "It'll tell you the latest position."

I watched him as he read through the paper, and noticed a furrow deepen on his brow. He looked up at me. "Do you mean to say that AFFE is cutting back on credit?" he asked. "Yes," I replied. "It's the only prudent course in the present environment."

He angrily crumpled the paper. "Don't you realise that the government's policy is to boost credit, not cut it back? This is entirely unacceptable. You must recall this memo immediately. I shall dictate a replacement. Credit must flow at any cost."

I suffered a moment of total confusion before I realised that he was, of course, completely right.

Fri 30 Jan: An early summons from Gershon. He looked annoyed.

"Parquet," he said, "I did not have a very jolly meeting with Grimm last night about executive remuneration policies.

"I gather you have misread the political smoke signals from Westminster. They are the masters now, and you can forget everything you ever learnt about prudent lending."

Parquet

Gershon blogs:

Mon 26 Jan: A New Year and a New Era dawns. Apparently the New Era will involve increased regulation, huge budget deficits and rapid growth in the public sector. Rather like the Old Era, then.

The New Year's Honours list includes several surprises – all of them unwelcome. Civil servants, regulators and all manner of time-serving reptiles abound. Given that salaries in the public sector, even before allowing for their lavish pensions, are now higher than in the private sector, can we look forward to a time when Tesco's delivery drivers are honoured for their "selfless dedication" in getting up at 5am to feed the nation? I doubt it somehow.

Tues 27 Jan: The much-thinned ranks of AFFE employees seem to have been largely unaffected by the loss of their erstwhile colleagues/ rivals/objects of romantic infatuation. Tony "Head of Security" Imbroglio is a case in point. He greets me warmly; apparently quite oblivious to how he clings to employment by a mere gossamer thread. Sleek and well fed, his immaculate coiffure of raven hair heavy with rancid oil, he exudes an entirely inappropriate aura of placid contentment. I scowl at him and he beams back.

Walking past the compliance area it's clearly business as usual. A new temp (why, for goodness sake are we still employing temps?) is busily Googling holiday websites. Pauline is preparing to tuck into a vast sack of carrots (New Year's resolution perhaps?). And where is Parquet? Nowhere to be seen; no doubt enjoying one of his numerous and lengthy unexplained absences.

Wed 28 Jan: Since the – I have to say, much needed – injection of public money into AFFE we have all become accustomed to a hefty postbag from sundry government departments.

These missives typically promise "co-operation", "shared vision and objectives" followed by demands for endless information and concluding with some barely-concealed threat or other.

Today, however, the process of ritual humiliation is being elevated to a higher level. We are to have our own Political Commissar. His name is James Grimm. He is 13 years old, has a dog called Flossie and is as keen as mustard. He will be working closely with Parquet in the compliance area. I explain to them both that I am expecting the need for only minimal interaction and that any questions or concerns should be directed to Parquet himself.

Thurs 29 Jan: Most of the day seems to have been taken up with trying to resolve details of Grimm's status.

Bridget, our HR Obergruppenführer, won't allow him a security pass because he's not a full-time employee while the process of signing him in as a visitor each day – bear in mind this is already day two – is "straining Security's resources to breaking point," according to Imbroglio.

Is there nothing trivial enough for these people to sort out on their own? Or could it just be that the ancient enmity between Bridget and Tony has come unscathed through the financial crisis?

Fri 30 Jan: As if the impertinent questions from Grimm about remuneration weren't annoying enough, it seems that Parquet has completely failed to understand anything of what has happened over the past six months. I'm sure that my impatience was starting to show as I explained it to him once again.

Over the last several years we extended loans to people who can't pay the money back. These are classified as Greedy Banker loans and are a bad thing.

We are now to extend loans to people who are even less likely to pay the money back because we are entering an economic depression. These are known as socially beneficial loans because they have been approved by a socialist.

What could be simpler than that?

Gershon

~

As the year progressed, the distress continued. AIG announced a quarterly loss of $61.7bn, the biggest in US corporate history. HSBC announced a $17.7bn rights issue to "strengthen capital". The US Federal Reserve said it would purchase $1.2 trillion of debt from the private sector to help boost lending and promote economic recovery.

In a further sign that the numbers were still getting bigger, the April G20 summit in London announced a further $1.1 trillion to help combat the economic consequences of the credit crunch. The IMF raised its estimates of total financial sector write-downs to $4 trillion, with more than half arising outside the US. Chancellor Alistair Darling predicted a UK budget deficit of £175bn – more than 10% of GDP. At AFFE the strain of the financial crisis continued to make itself felt, with acrimony springing up between James Grimm and AFFE's temperamental security apparatus.

~

Bipolar banking

Parquet blogs:

Mon 23 Feb: It's been more than a month since AFFE was forced to grovel to the government for a £10bn bail-out, and I don't know whether to laugh or cry. I laugh because it's kept us alive and humiliated our useless management. I cry because I now have to share an office with James Grimm, the Treasury stooge who has been appointed to keep an eye on us.

Grimm is one of those blank-eyed civil service types who never return civilities. You ask him how he is and he says "fine thank you" without asking you the same. I suppose it's his pathetic way of trying to look superior.

Grimm's main purpose in life is to ensure that AFFE keeps lending money to bankrupt people and businesses: anything to keep the economy going. He has demanded to see all loan applications, and stamps "APPROVED" on every single one. When I ask him: "But who's going to cover our losses?" he gives me a blank stare. "The shareholders," he says.

I'm not a political man by nature, but I'm learning fast and I don't like it.

Tues 24 Feb: *11am.* Even Pauline, my assistant, whose only activity is to daub her face with cream and eat sweets all day, is unsettled. "How long have we got him for?" she whispered, emitting a gale of pear drops. "For the duration," I reply.

A short while later, during one of Grimm's mysterious absences (slipping off to Whitehall for a quick report?), Tony Imbroglio, our highly-strung head of security, comes in – IN TEARS! The head of security in tears. "That government man," he sobs. "He breaks all the rules and tells me I'm no good!"

This can't go on. I shall speak to Gershon.

2pm. When I called on Gershon he seemed unexpectedly jolly. "Well, Parquet," he said. "How are you getting on with young James? A fine fellow. Destined for great things on the slippery pole. What!"

I explained that Grimm was uncivil, was destroying our loan book and had upset Imbroglio and Pauline. Gershon was unmoved. "Stick with him, Parquet, we have no choice." He then leant forward with a conspiratorial wink. "And make sure he complies fully with all the regulations!"

I quickly realised that was a brilliant idea.

Wed 25 Feb: I was ready for Grimm when he came in, black Whitehall briefcase in hand.

"Mr Grimm," I said. "Just a formality, but FSA regulations require everyone who approves loans to read and sign the *Competent Persons Declaration*." Grimm looked puzzled, but said "OK". I passed him the Declaration, all 120 pages of it. That kept him quiet for a bit. After he had signed it with an impatient flourish, he made for the door.

I blocked his way. "I'm sorry," I said. "Just one or two more things." Grimm and I spent a happy morning reading and signing the *AFFE Credit Procedures Manual* (250 pages), the *Basel 2 Capital Adequacy Accord* (750 pages), the *Markets in Financial Instruments Directive* (3,000 pages), and the *Respect at Work* handbook (250 pages) which Bridget, our head of HR, wrote and insists that all AFFE personnel read.

All the while I was effusively apologetic. "It's mad, I know," I said trying to sound sympathetic. "But this government is very keen on compliance, and as for Brussels, don't get me started..."

Grimm was gone all afternoon, which permitted me to have a quiet word with Tony and Pauline.

Thurs 26 Feb: Grimm had only been at his desk a few minutes when Imbroglio came by carrying a metal case. "Ah Mr Grimm," he beamed. "Just a few security formalities!" Out of his case he pulled a load of electronic apparatus and pointed it at Grimm's face. A bright light flashed causing Grimm to blink in pain. "Iris recognition, yes, very good!" He then grabbed Grimm's hand and pressed his fingers into an inkpad. "Fingerprints! Yes." A look of annoyance began to cross Grimm's face.

Tony then produced a thick manual. "I need to ask you questions about your background – for the anti-terrorism regulations, you understand." A very personal probing followed to which Grimm protested: "But I'm from the Treasury!" Tony persisted. "Sorry, everybody must answer." There wasn't much left of the morning by the time he had finished.

Pauline got going in the afternoon, and she can talk the wheels off a cart. By tea time, Grimm and I had heard all about her family, the neighbours, their children, their illnesses, their holiday plans, what they thought of the government and that nasty Mr Brown. The office was thick with the smell of sweets and cheap perfume. I glanced at Grimm, who was sweating and clutching the sides of his desk. Suddenly, he screamed "I can't stand this any more!" and charged for the door.

Fri 27 Feb: No sign of Grimm this morning. I wonder where he got to. The phone rang, it was Gershon.

"Good work Parquet."

Parquet

Gershon blogs:

Mon 23 Feb: Month two of year zero. Capitalism has been abolished. Strategic industries are now under state direction. Greedy Kulaks (aka Greedy Bankers) hoarding credit have been identified as the cause of ongoing shortages of money. Political commissars have already been despatched to every enterprise to ensure compliance with government directives. Doubtless, gangs of young "workers" will shortly be urged to wreak summary justice on the enemies of the people. Strangely, a look at my latest executive AFFE stock option valuation statement shows little evidence of successful hoarding. Quite the opposite, in fact.

Tues 24 Feb: Here at AFFE, James "Jim" Grimm (what were his parents thinking of?) from the Treasury is the vanguard of the new socialist revolution. I have encouraged him to work closely with Parquet so that they can prioritise things together, add appendices to the

relevant manuals and so on, without needing to come anywhere near my office.

I have also included Grimm in the Human Resources Annual Planning Process.
Respect at Work 2009 is already starting
to take shape in spite of the fact that there
is an ever-dwindling number of AFFE
employees available either to respect
or disrespect one another. To add to the
sense of surrealistic horror, Bridget seems

to have taken quite a shine to Master Grimm and becomes positively
coquettish whenever he appears. Grimm appears immune to her charms,
so perhaps he is partly human after all.

Wed 25 Feb: The dream-like (for "dream-like" read "nightmare-like")
quality of the post-credit-crunch world became even more pronounced
after yesterday's audience with Parquet. He is fed up with Grimm's
assumption that nothing can happen in the bank without his approval –
something which, it hardly needs to be said, is not forthcoming without
the most unimaginably longwinded approval process. Parquet is also
increasingly irritated by the idle sweet-eating habits of Pauline, deputy
compliance officer. What this means is that Grimm has become the new
Parquet and that Parquet (oh! inestimable horror!) is turning into me.
So, if Parquet is me, then who am I? This is ridiculous, I'm really too
old for an existential crisis on this scale.

Thurs 26 Feb: Like Hume leaving his study to join his family at
breakfast and finding that his doubts about the existence of the
external world immediately disappeared, I find that my identity crisis
is quickly solved by a couple of hours working on my book *The
Adventures of Chevalier Robert*. It's very good indeed. No longer am I

Edward Gershon, Greedy Banker and CEO of "beleaguered" AFFE – I am Ed Gershon, wit, raconteur, best-selling children's author, creator of some of the nation's (nay the world's!) best-loved characters. The only thing that remains to be done is to find a publisher. That should be easy.

Fri 27 Feb: Parquet rings me to tell me that Grimm has gone home in tears. Apparently he couldn't stand it any more. I know how he feels.
Gershon

~

A new regime

Parquet blogs:
Mon 23 Mar: This business of being owned by Her Majesty's Treasury is driving me to distraction.

It's four months since AFFE received a £10bn government bail-out, and I frankly don't have the first idea what we're supposed to do. The taxpayer owns 60 per cent of the bank, but have we been nationalised? Oh no, says the Treasury. AFFE is temporarily in the safe-keeping of the state until it can be returned to the private sector.

But if we're 60 per cent owned by the state, does the government have a say in how we run the business? Oh no, says the Treasury. We don't get involved in commercial decisions. Then why do we have Mr James Grimm, a Treasury official, sitting in my office all day long watching over every move we make?

Are we being punished for our "misbehaviour"? Oh no, says the Treasury. Then why does Mr Grimm want to know all about the bank's bonus plans, its dividend plans, even its pension plans?

Are the banks supposed to be back on the path of prudence? Oh yes, says the Treasury. Then why does Mr Grimm force us to keep lending money to bankrupt homeowners and businesses?

And yours truly is supposed to run a Sound Compliance Regime? Consistent, disciplined, fair? You can see why I'm tearing my hair out. It's going to be either drink or pills. Probably both.

Tues 24 Mar: Very embarrassing…

I was walking down the hall this morning when I bumped into Gershon. He looked me up and down. "Parquet," he said, "you look terrible. You should go and have a check-up."

"Yes, Mr Gershon," I said. "I don't know how to cope with all this stress."

Gershon put his arm round me in his condescending way. "Do like me," he said. "Treat it all as a great big joke. After all, it's not often that the jolly old Treasury gives you £10bn with no expectation of getting it back. Just relax. And enjoy it. There's a good Parquet."

I can't stand the man's arrogance, in treating me like a child and the taxpayer like an idiot. Maybe total cynicism is the only way to survive. But I'm not that type. Too conscientious.

I fixed up to have a medical on Thursday.

Wed 25 Mar: James Grimm came into my office bright and early and sat down with his usual impassive stare. He opened his black Whitehall briefcase and handed me a packet. "Today's required reading," he said. "We need your response ASAP." He got up and was gone.

"HM TREASURY. THE FUTURE OF FINANCIAL REGULATION IN THE UK," I read. "Recent events have exposed weaknesses in the UK's system of financial regulation. This paper lays out proposals to enhance and strengthen… blah… blah… blah."

Normally this sort of stuff would have me salivating with excitement:

new regulations, yards of them, all wonderful grist to my Compliance Mill! Today, I could only think: "What a load of rubbish." Every time we patch up a crisis, we only lay the ground for an even bigger one down the road. Welcome to the crash of 2015.

I chucked it in the bin. I'm learning the Gershon method.

Thurs 26 Mar: Down to the bowels of the building to the bank's clinic. The nurse there is always bright and breezy. In her little bunker, she obviously doesn't know that the world above ground has been nuked.

"Mr Parquet? You've come for a check-up? Take a seat please," she said pointing to the waiting room. I passed through the door and saw, to my astonishment, John Sutton, the finance director, Bridget, the head of HR, even Tony Imbroglio, the head of security, all sitting in a row, staring into nothingness.

"Here for a check-up?" I asked. They all nodded. What is this place coming to?

I'm not sure why I bothered, really. The doctor said there was nothing wrong with me that a long week-end's rest wouldn't cure. "You should learn to relax," he said. "Leave the worrying to others." The Gershon method is spreading.

Fri 27 Mar: When I came into my office this morning, everything looked different. The shelves full of compliance manuals were still there, so was my desk with its screen and in-trays. But it was a stage set. It didn't mean anything any more. I suddenly felt on top of the world.

I called Gershon's office to let him know. His PA took the call. "Mr Gershon has been told by his doctors to take a rest cure," she said. "He'll be away for a fortnight." How strange. Nobody cares any more.
Parquet

Gershon blogs:

Mon 23 Mar: Month three of year zero. After the declaration of a State of National Emergency the banking system has been placed under state control. The rest of the economy is to follow shortly. Contract law is to be replaced by People's Revolutionary Justice or "the Court of Public Opinion" in the words of Ms Harriet Harman, self-appointed Chairperson of the Committee for Public Safety. Here at AFFE things are very confusing. Even compliance-hungry Parquet is increasingly unclear with what he should comply. The loathsome Jim Grimm, the Treasury's man on the spot, has once again assumed his habitual Sphinx-like demeanour after his emotional outburst last month. He is absolutely no help.

Tues 24 Mar: Early-morning conference call with the Singaporeans (requested by them, of course). They want to "review the status of their investment". That triumphant trip to Singapore in which, against all odds, I pulled a huge rabbit out of the hat thereby securing (as I fondly thought) the long-term future of AFFE seems to belong to a distant time – it's hard to believe that it was only last year.

I don't know what to suggest. Perhaps they would like to fly over and we could visit the grave. We could even disinter the tiny mummified body of what was once the mega rabbit and perform some sort of ceremony of remembrance. I know that visits to shrines and suchlike are very popular in the Far East.

I'm about to make this friendly suggestion when John Sutton, our CFO, intervenes and drones on for what seems like hours. I tune out. Every so often the phrase "subordinated in the capital structure" penetrates my reverie. On my way back to my office I encounter Parquet. He really is a horrid little man.

Wed 25 Mar: Executive Committee. Our part in the Programme for National Economic Recovery involves a commitment to expand our loan book. These new loans will be socially responsible and will restore the flow of credit to the economy. Under no circumstances are they to be confused with the economically damaging Greedy Banker loans that were so sadly prevalent as recently as last year. John raises the important question of a loan that was approved in the Greedy Banker era but which has not yet been drawn down.

If the borrower now draws down the facility, is the loan a Greedy Banker (GB) loan or a Socially Responsible (SR) loan? I suggest that we bring in Jim Grimm and ask him for his expert exegesis. Bridget then points out that since there will be no bonuses at AFFE such a loan cannot be a GB loan and must therefore be an SR loan. Others look less convinced and we decide to minute the observation and apply to the Treasury for clarification.

Thurs 26 Mar: No doubt as part of *Respect at Work, Year Zero* Bridget has convinced me that all senior staff should have a compulsory medical. Quite what the quacks expect to discover is a mystery but apparently we would be acting as a "responsible employer" given the levels of stress under which "key personnel" have been operating. I'm not surprised to learn that no one seems to be suffering any ill-effects whatsoever. I was, however, very surprised to discover that Parquet and the almost inconceivably idle Imbroglio are "key personnel".

Fri 27 Mar: I'm going to take some time off. The role of CEO seems to have largely disappeared under the new regime and the confusion about exactly what we are trying to achieve is enough to drive one insane.

How can it be a triumph for Northern Rock to have repaid some of its borrowings from the government one month and a triumph that it is expanding its lending the next? Talk about a split personality. Bipolar Banking. I like it. It's got a winning ring.

Gershon

~

May's signal event was Chrysler, one of the US "Big Three" auto makers, filing for bankruptcy. A month later General Motors did the same and was thenceforth known as "Government Motors". The UK Treasury Committee of MPs said that bankers rather than policymakers or the general public were responsible for the economic crisis. Sir Fred Goodwin, ex-chief of RBS and architect of its demise, attracted particular opprobrium for the size of his pension. Edward Gershon, CEO of AFFE, also attracted some unwelcome attention. Subsequently, revelations about MPs' systematic abuse of their expenses system allowed them to displace bankers as the most reviled group in British society. The US Treasury announced that ten of the biggest US banks had failed their *stress tests and that they required a further $74.6bn in capital.*

After June's Chapter 11 filing, General Motors bondholders received 10 cents in the dollar. The US government loaned the company another $50bn. Wide lending spreads and reduced competition resulted in record investment banking profits in the first quarter of 2009 and some banks were able to repay the emergency funding provided by the government, a move encouraged by the restrictions on corporate pay imposed on entities receiving public support. AFFE's Gershon tested the water but thought better of it when he heard of Grimm's apoplectic reaction.

~

Pension fury

Parquet blogs:

Mon 27 April: All hell is about to break loose, I just know it. On Wednesday, we publish our annual report, and it will contain the latest details of the pensions accumulating to top executives. That's not good news for a bank that lost £10bn and survives on life support from the British taxpayer.

Being in Compliance, I know all the gory details because I have to check the annual report for Regulatory Accuracy. I saw, for example, that Gershon has a pot worth several million that will give him a pension of hundreds of thousands of pounds a year.

All perfectly legit, signed and sealed years ago when AFFE was flying high. But totally inappropriate to our current crippled state.

I doubt that it has even occurred to Gershon that all this might be controversial. He still struts around as if the bank owes him favours – and not just the bank but the country at large. Maybe I should talk to him. I called his PA and set up a meeting in the morning.

Tues 28 April: The meeting did not go well. I knocked on his door. "Well, Parquet, what is it?"

"I thought we should have a word about your pension, sir." (I hate calling him sir. I feel servile, but I lack the guts to call him Gershon or even Edward. Oh, how he lords it over me!)

"What's that to do with you?"

"I thought we should be prepared to deal with tomorrow's annual report release. It might cause a stir."

"Of course it won't. People are bored stiff by pensions. Even if it does, it's none of their business. The terms of my pension were agreed years ago by the board. It's contractually bound."

And so it went on. I tried to point out that a country in economic crisis, heading for the financial abyss, might not see it that way. But he just got angry.

Eventually he stood up. "Parquet," he said in commanding tones. "Will you kindly leave my office?" ·

I quit. But I'm not going to give up.

Wed 29 April: The first thing I did this morning was call Kroll and arrange for extra security round Gershon's house. The mob will be smashing his windows and slashing his tyres by the end of the day. He might at least be grateful for that.

I had hardly put the phone down when Bridget, the head of HR, came running over in a complete fluster. Normally, I can't stand Bridget, domineering and self-righteous, a believer in "the value of values", whatever that means. But I suddenly realised she was an ally.

"I've seen the report," she gasped. "We have to do something." I explained that Gershon was deaf to pleas. "Leave it to me," she said, and strode off down the hall.

She was back within 10 minutes. "That man is impossible," she said through clenched teeth. "This is a total disaster." I had to fight the feeling of pleasure at the sight of Bridget brought low. But we were now the good guys.

I spent the afternoon clutching my desk.

Thurs 30 April: Sure enough. It's all over the papers this morning.

"Greedy Grabber," headlined *The Sun*. "Fat cat banker Edward Gershon, boss of debt-ridden AFFE bank, is getting a multi-million pension payout.

From the taxpayer.

His bank has already had £10bn of our money.

So why should he get any more? The Sun tracked him down to his luxury City office but Greedy Grabber Gershon told our reporter: 'It's none of your business.'

What planet is he living on?"

It's horrific. The phones are ringing all over the place. Angry crowds are gathering outside the building and Kroll has erected barriers around the house.

Bridget joins me, lips pursed, and we go along to Gershon's office to plead for a gesture before it's too late. He is on the phone and waves us out. We can hear the conversation.

"Yes, prime minister, I hear what you are saying. But this is a contract and I'm sticking with it." Pause. "...and I hope you have a happy retirement too." He slammed the phone down. "Interfering so-and-so," he muttered and headed for the back exit.

Bridget broke down in tears and I put my arm around her, something I never imagined I would do.

Fri 1 May: Thank heavens the Bank Holiday's coming up. It will give me time to reflect.

The question on my mind is not so much how someone can be as pig-headed about money as Gershon, but where he thinks he's heading. What sort of retirement awaits someone who has become an object of public loathing, who will be recognised wherever he goes as the man who walked off with millions of pounds of undeserved public money? Surely not a happy one.

If only he'd listened to me on Tuesday morning. I could have helped him to end his days in peace and contentment.

Instead he faces hell. He deserves it.

Parquet

Gershon blogs:

Mon 27 Apr: Through Government diktat, banking has been permanently changed for the better. Our new lending now consists entirely of Socially Responsible loans. These loans may or may not be paid back but have been properly approved by a socialist government. In our particular case they have been cheered on their way by the charmless Jim Grimm of H.M. Treasury, a man of unimpeachable integrity and entirely free of the ambition and greed which characterises the private sector.

Tues 28 Apr: Whereas the Greedy Banker/Ambitious Little Sod Grimm distinction is one that would once have taxed the world's greatest philosophers, in this annus mirabilis greater mysteries are daily revealed. In Mr Geithner's latest plan to save the world's financial system, public and private investors contribute to a pool which then leverages up to the gills to buy distressed assets from the banking system. Apparently risk is then apportioned asymmetrically to different classes of investors. Never can a solution have so closely resembled the problem that it was designed to solve.

These reveries and others are rudely interrupted by the announcement that the wretched Parquet has come to see me about "an urgent matter of considerable importance". The description "a tiresome matter of complete inconsequence" has in the past more accurately described most of his interventions and so indeed it proves on this occasion. For some unknown reason he has come to ask me about my pension. I ask him to leave.

Wed 29 Apr: As I leave my house I'm confronted by a car full of goons one of whom opens the door and walks up to me, his hand outstretched. My initial – and most uncomfortable – reaction is that this might be related to one of our eastern European business ventures and that these are mates of Boris. The truth is more banal. It is, of course, another of Parquet's diabolical schemes and the goons are from Kroll who have come to protect me; from what, exactly? They seem to have no idea.

Today it's Bridget's turn to come and annoy me about my pension; apparently it could become a "focus of public indignation". She seems upset about something – presumably Grimm has spurned her ever more desperate advances. What is this growing obsession with my pension? After lunch some reptile from *The Sun* rings me with a whole lot of impertinent questions. Naturally I tell him where to go.

Thurs 30 Apr: Finance Committee. I stop to collect my papers from John's office. The centre of attention is a misshapen carrot and, yes, with considerable imagination, it does look as if it has sprouted a male member. "It's the credit crunch carrot," says his simpering deputy, noticing my admiring glance. Oh Merrie England! While the amusing vegetable is still revered, sainted Albion is safe!

By lunchtime it's less than merry in front of AFFE headquarters. An angry mob has formed protesting against... yes you guessed it. At last! The moment for which I have been waiting for 15 years. Tony "Head

of Security" Imbroglio has finally got something to do.

To add to the sense of mounting surreality the prime minister's office rings to ask me if I would consider giving up my pension. Why would I do that? Upon inquiry it appears that the politicians and regulators who oversaw this mess are not giving up theirs. As a large taxpayer I was however heartened to be told that Mr Jacqui Smith's tireless pounding of the constituency beat is not yet a pensionable activity.

Long weekend ahead, I'm retiring, ho ho, to the country. I think I'll ask for the car at the back entrance.

Fri 1 May: In the timeless expression of Anglophone workers every-where – Thank God it's Friday.
Gershon

An anniversary

Parquet blogs:

Mon 25 May: It's more than a year since I put up "WALK – DON'T RUN" notices in all the hallways, and I'm pleased to report that the number of collisions between people and trolleys has been halved. When I mentioned this to Gershon, he put me down as he always does. "That's because we have half the number of people and trolleys," he said.

I shall not be discouraged. I have now set a target of reducing collisions by a greater percentage than staff lay-offs. This will give us what economists call "a reduction in real terms". I am certain that the result of this will be higher staff morale and lower surgery costs.

I am also considering not taking a holiday this year. It seems wrong for staff of a bank that has received a £10bn state bail-out to go gallivanting about the place at the taxpayer's expense.

Besides, with the business in its present fragile condition, I might be needed to man the pumps. Can't trust anyone else to do it.

I got Pauline to pin a holiday rota on the wall and I wrote next to my name: "No holiday this year". Someone needs to set an example. Unfortunately, that was not how Deirdre saw it when I got home. "What a fool you are, Arnold," she said. "You make all these personal sacrifices when the reality is that it's every man for himself."

Tues 26 May: When I got into the office this morning, I found James Grimm, the Treasury's unpleasant resident watchman, looking at the holiday rota. I hoped he would be impressed by my devotion to duty but he cast me a pitying glance. "Personally," he said, "I shall be taking the whole of August off." I fear Deirdre was right.

Wed 27 May: Gershon's PA called me first thing. "He wants to see you, now," she said curtly.

I walked into his office and found him leafing through a thick file with John Sutton, the finance director (who ought to be lined up with Gershon and shot for getting us into this mess).

"Ah Parquet," he said. "You get on with Grim Jim, don't you?" Before I could say no, he went on: "I want you to convey some news to him.

"As you know, AFFE took advantage of the government's bail-out plan to raise a spot of extra capital. We didn't really need it, but if some-one offers you money on a plate, you take it.

"A lot has changed since then. AFFE has had a healthy shake-out, the economy is looking up, and frankly we feel we can run a better business without the Treasury breathing down our necks. John and I have worked out a plan to raise capital from the markets and buy ourselves out.

"We'll be free again. Won't that be wonderful? Grim Jim can pack his bags and go home. Would you kindly go and tell him."

I couldn't understand why Gershon didn't go and break this impor-tant piece of news to Jim himself. It sounded a tremendous idea: put AFFE back on its own two feet, hand money back to the Treasury to spend on more deserving causes, ease the national budget – and get Grim Jim out of my hair.

Grimm was out, as he usually is, sneaking on us to his masters, no doubt. I'll have to wait till tomorrow to see him.

Thurs 28 May: I very quickly learnt why Gershon made me the messenger.

Grimm's face boiled

in fury. "Utterly, totally out of the question," he fumed. "Who do you people think you are, thinking that you can escape the Treasury's clutches that easily?

"Why do you think we invested in you? Out of kindness, to stop you going bust? No! It's to bend you to our will! There will be no buy-outs, no first-class tickets back to the private sector, no return to the bonus trough. This is nationalisation, and that's how it's going to stay! You go and tell all that to your corrupt and useless bosses!"

Grimm was sweating and waving his arms like some fascist dictator. I collapsed into a gaping heap. When I got home that night, I admitted to Deirdre that she was right and I was wrong. I would book some holiday for July.

Fri 29 May: Gershon telephoned me very early, before I could get to the holiday rota. "Well?" he asked rather rudely.

I described the scene. "Just as well," he said. "It means I can now safely take the whole of June, July and August off." I was stunned into silence.

Gershon gave one of his cruel cackles. "Pauline tells me you've generously offered to stick around all summer." I tried to tell him of my new plans, but he cut in. "No modesty, please. It's very noble of you." The phone went dead.

Parquet

Gershon blogs:

Mon 25 May: While others mark the anniversary of the death of capitalism or lament the rise of James Grimm and his ilk from the swamps of Whitehall, Parquet is celebrating the successful completion of his "Walk don't run" campaign. The campaign is now 12 months old and has, he tells me, brought untold benefits to AFFE. What exactly those benefits are is not entirely clear. Of course this is no longer the right sort of question. In the pithy phrase of Liz, our unkempt and faintly malodorous "change facilitator" (also kindly provided to us by Whitehall), "a target achieved is a benefit conferred".

Tues 26 May: Bridget tells me that Liz would like to "observe" the monthly human resources meeting. Apparently "effective human resources management is the key to effective change management". The answer is NOT A CHANCE. Bridget calls me back. My answer proved unacceptable because "a working knowledge of the human resource process is essential to maintaining change momentum", and Liz is confident that I wouldn't act in a way that frustrated our shared objectives. Since we don't have any shared objectives this hardly constitutes much of an argument, but even in the unlikely event of us sharing said objectives the answer would still be ABSOLUTELY NOT. Bridget sounded quite pleased.

Wed 27 May: All-day meeting with John, our CFO. First-quarter trading profits have been exceptional. Huge corporate bond issuance and massively wide spreads have certainly helped. The big profit opening, however, has been the opportunity to unwind complex positions with, shall we say, less than streetwise government sponsored entities on the other side of the trade. When you add it all up and throw in some additional new capital, it could just amount to a ticket to freedom. I wonder how our new masters would react. Before pursuing the suggestion through the proper channels I'll put a ferret down the hole and see what happens. In this sort of situation a ferret you are happy never to see again is a sensible choice. Parquet it is.

Thurs 28 May: A strange silence has fallen. Parquet is usually quick to bother me with the most inconsequential trivia but, typically, on one of those rare occasions when he has been given a real job to do there is no feedback at all. It would be nice to think that he and Grimm had confronted one another in some subterranean corner and torn each other apart, never to see the light of day again, but I fear this is just wishful thinking.

Fri 29 May: I give in and ring up the wretched creature to find out what went on. Apparently, when Parquet outlined our potential bid for freedom Grimm threw a total wobbly and started to shriek, foam at the mouth, speak in tongues, etc, etc. That gives me some idea of the reception we are likely to get at the higher echelons. Best leave a preliminary approach until after the summer and give everyone an opportunity to cool their heels.

Sounds like the opportunity for a long, relaxing break. Parquet can mind the fort, his life is one long holiday anyway.

Who knows? He and Liz might discover some shared objectives.

Gershon

~

Wimbledon

Parquet blogs:

Mon 22 June: Wimbledon time of year again. At least no one from AFFE will be going: it would be a disgraceful misuse of taxpayers' money after our £10bn government bail-out. Anyway I, for one, have far more pressing demands on my time, not least ensuring that AFFE plays its part in getting the country back on its feet.

Despite all the talk of green shoots, we are still far from turning the corner. Everywhere I look there is fear and uncertainty. The brighter numbers must be treated with the utmost caution. It will be a long and painful process.

Tues 23 June: Gershon has scheduled a senior staff meeting tomorrow morning. I wonder what it can be about? There is much speculation in the bank that he will be launching a new initiative to restore profitability.

One thing AFFE can do for the taxpayer is cut its costs. OK, I know that compliance costs are a big part of the budget. But that's different. Compliance keeps the business on the road. People really need to understand just how vital the Compliance Function is. I will prepare a presentation for tomorrow's meeting entitled: "Regulatory Compliance: The Path to Profits!"

I put the idea to James Grimm (Grim Jim). I expected him to make encouraging noises, but he seemed strangely unenthusiastic. "Go for it, Parquet," he said with a yawn. The stress is obviously getting to him.

Wed 24 June: I can't believe it! The command from on high is "Full steam ahead!"

There we were: the heads of investment banking, retail banking, fund management, marketing, HR, PR, and compliance, etc, with Gershon grinning like the fat cat that he is. Beside him was Wharton Graff, the bank's creepy chief economist.

Gershon waved for silence. "All the indications are that we have turned the corner," he said. "In fact we are already past the green shoots stage and well into the bursting buds stage, with the blossom stage in sight. Isn't that right, Wharton?" Wharton gave an ingratiating smile. "That's right chief! Our markets are firming up beautifully. All our economic models point to a sharp recovery in the second half, leading to boom conditions in 2010. By then we'll be well past the blossom stage into the golden apples stage.

"There you are," cried Gershon, rubbing his hands in glee. "I want AFFE to grab every one of those golden apples. Go for it boys! The bonus meter starts today!"

I have never seen such a display of utter recklessness. I stood up to object. "But Mr Gershon, sir…" He rounded on me. "Parquet, please attend to your compliance manuals. That will be all."

Thurs 25 June: I'm still in a state of shock. Yesterday's performance was not only an utter disgrace, but clear evidence that the reckless culture that drove this bank to the brink of bankruptcy is still alive and well.

I have to put the brakes on this madness, or Gershon will drive the bank right over the cliff. My duty was clear: I called on Grim Jim. He was still yawning. "Gershon is driving this bank to ruin," I said. "You must put a stop to it!" Jim leant across the desk. "Parquet, I begin a month's annual leave tomorrow and frankly I couldn't give a toss." So much for our "partners" in Whitehall.

Fri 26 June: I shall have to tackle this one more directly. Overnight, I resolved to contact all the department heads individually to reason with them. The economy has NOT turned the corner; it would be crazy to move aggressively back into the markets; talk of bonuses is a complete illusion…

I started with Will Barrow, head of investment banking. "He's not here," said his PA. I asked her to get Barrow to give me a call.

Next, I tried the head of retail banking. Same thing; not there; left a message. And so it was with all the others: fund management, marketing, even Wharton Graff, none of them was anywhere to be found.

Very mysterious. It was as if the entire sixth floor had been wiped out by some 9/11-style attack.

In desperation, I called Gershon to tackle him head on. "Mr Gershon is out all day," said his PA. "He's taken the lads to Wimbledon. He hoped you wouldn't mind keeping an eye on the bank for the day."

The problem with being in the Compliance Department is that you develop a sense of responsibility which is so superior to that of everyone else that you occasionally start to lose touch with reality.

I checked the BBC website and was pleased to see that the weather forecast for south-west London is heavy rain all afternoon.

Parquet

Gershon blogs:

Mon 22 June: The sun is shining. It's Wimbledon week and all around us green shoots are sprouting. Providing one doesn't think too hard about the socialist revolution evidenced by: a) the nationalisation of most banks; b) the nationalisation of GM (Government Motors); and c) government borrowing on a scale not even seen in wartime and stretching out as far as the crack of doom, then one could almost feel upbeat. In fact I'm almost certain that I heard John Sutton humming "Happy days are here again" under his breath as I passed him in the corridor this morning. Beyond belief.

Tues 23 June: Human resources monthly meeting. Due to the fact that bonuses are now politically incorrect, it's going to be pay rises all round for the remaining lucky boys and girls of AFFE. Whatever happened to "Variable compensation – a strategy for flexibility"? I ask Bridget. She doesn't seem particularly amused. Recalibrating pay scales, adjusting pension contributions, setting new scales for allowable expenses and, doubtless, framing a new set of policies on Diversity, Respect at Work etc, etc, promise many happy hours of busy work ahead. She might at least look a bit brighter at the prospect.

Wed 24 June: The fact is that, however hopeless the outlook, there is no point in moping around while Grimm gnaws at one's soul. "Once more unto the breach," and so forth. I have summoned AFFE's finest for a rousing session of shock and awe. We will seize the manifold opportunities presented by The Triumph of World Socialism. We will never surrender.

In honour of the occasion I have had AFFE's chief economist specially exhumed. Goebbels he most certainly isn't, I think sadly. The bloodless figure shuffles to the front of the room and the skeletal hands of the undead grip the sides of the podium for support. A reedy voice issues forth. For this is the ludicrously named Wharton Graff. How did he survive the pogroms and bloodletting of the last year? I ask myself. I make a mental note to have a word with Bridget. Surely this strangely unsettling figure is not somehow under her protection?

Wharton's models – presumably the same ones that so egregiously failed to predict the slump – now promise us "Golden Apples" whatever those are. I relieve him of the microphone before the metaphors become any harder to understand and then, as is the custom, I ritually exhort the crowd and then make to dismiss them. Wait, there is a question. I don't remember inviting questions. It is Parquet. How I hate him.

Thurs 25 June: A rare gap in my calendar allows me the opportunity to catch up with James Grimm and to benefit from his insights. How does he feel about the parliamentary expenses scandal? Does he welcome the forthcoming transparency about the pay and benefits of civil servants? Exactly how long will he be taking off this summer? When will he be leaving the bank? All are subjects on which we have a full and frank exchange of views.

Fri 26 June: Wimbledon. Warm and balmy. I'm sipping a cold glass

of champagne when a cloud passes in front of the sun. Was that Grimm heading for the best seats on Centre Court? I look again; there's no doubt about it.

Gershon

~

Poison squid redux

Parquet blogs:

Mon 24 August: What an awful day. The holidays are over (it was Blackpool this year to save money) and I'm back in the Realm of Recklessness, the Ghetto of Greed, the Epicentre of Egomania. (I already feel better by writing all that.)

One thing about holidays, you get to meet people, ordinary decent folk who are trying to make their way in life with families, mortgages and pets. Deirdre and I talked to lots of them in Blackpool, down in the seafront cafes and in the caravan park. They're all worried to death about their jobs, their children's jobs. They're frightened about their savings: will they have any left, and are they safe in the bank? Will life ever get better again?

Of course, they blamed greedy bankers for their plight, which put me badly on the spot. I was a complete coward when people asked me what I did for a living: I said I was in health and safety for a big company. I couldn't possibly admit the truth.

But I don't feel responsible for the terrible mess we're in. I spent three years trying to get AFFE to take risk seriously, to no avail whatsoever. It's not my fault that Gershon and the rest of his rotten management have utterly no sense of responsibility.

I can hear Gershon's loud laugh down the hall. How I hate the man.

Tues 25 August: I've had an idea.

This crisis is such a unique event that we must learn the right lessons from it. We must make sure it never happens again. I'm the man to do that. I shall compile a report: *Lessons from the crisis*, and circulate it to management, the board, the entire staff. Better still, I shall publish it! It will be my great service to society. The Parquet Report – alongside the Bischoff Report, the Walker Report, the Wigley Report, and the rest.

I told James Grimm (Grim Jim), our Treasury guardian, of my plan, thinking that he might recommend me to Alastair Darling. But he seemed curiously uninterested. Undaunted, though, I shall start on my report tomorrow.

Wed 26 August: I couldn't get started because Gershon called a management meeting to discuss the interim results. What a performance! Our revered boss looked pleased as Punch as he announced that AFFE had made a billion pounds in the first half. A BILLION POUNDS! Apparently this was because of the strong rise in the markets mid-summer and the huge margins now to be made on lending.

I couldn't believe it. They must be cooking the books.

To crown it all, Gershon announced that everyone is to get a salary increase. "We can't pay bonuses because of our political masters," he said casting an eye at Grim Jim. "But there's nothing to stop us raising pay!" There were whoops of joy from the assembled company, in with which I did not join.

I came away, gritting my teeth and determined to write a devastating report.

Thurs 27 August: I'm making good progress. My chapter headings are: Strong Compliance, Strong Risk Management, Strong Governance, Strong Incentive Structures, and Strong Social Responsibility. This report will really get to the heart of the problem and say things that have never been said before, with deep insights and tough recommendations.

I was interrupted by another summons from Gershon. This time it was to announce that AFFE has reached a deal with the Treasury to buy itself out of the government bail-out. With Grim Jim smiling beside him, Gershon said gleefully that AFFE "will be free by the end of the year". Again there were whoops of joy. Later, I said to Grim Jim: "That's a turnaround". Grim Jim replied: "We need the money".

I got on with my report, gritting my teeth even harder.

Fri 28 August: The Parquet Report is finished!

And what a piece of work! The accumulated wisdom of three years of hard knocks. There are no fewer than 39 bullet points, each a gem in its own way. I particularly like the final one: "Every bank must place the Compliance Function at the very heart of its operations." It couldn't be more crystal clear.

I printed up several copies and took one round to Gershon. He, more than anyone, needs to digest its wisdom.

He was sitting at his desk gloating over a big box of cigars. "A gift from a Russian client who has become very rich thanks to our recent investment advice," he said. "These are good markets if you have an inside track."

I concealed my disgust, and handed over my report. "I feel you should read this," I said.

Gershon read the title. "Lessons from the crisis, by Arnold Parquet." He looked up at me. "Crisis? What crisis? I don't remember any crisis. AFFE is operating perfectly normally."

He picked up my report and dropped it in the bin. "Have a nice weekend, Parquet."

Parquet

Gershon blogs:

Mon 24 August: What a difference a few months make. In January we went cap in hand to the Treasury. In February their minions arrived to take possession of the Socialist State's new prize. In March we were staring into the abyss and here we are in August paying back the loans and shepherding Commissar James Grimm, Change Facilitator Liz and doubtless untold legions of other public officials who have infiltrated AFFE towards the exit and the well-deserved obscurity of the stews of Whitehall.

Tues 25 August: Interim results day tomorrow – it looks as if it will be a very happy day indeed. Sorry though we all are that Grimm will shortly be leaving us, it's nice that he will be here to enjoy the announcement in person.

Wed 26 August: The number is a big one. One billion pounds in the first half. The stuff you couldn't give away last year has soared in value. Emerging market equities, leveraged loans and junk bonds are all back to where they were before Lehmans went down. Moreover, our lending margins have rocketed as the competition has been carried out. A happy day indeed.

Naturally, everyone was delighted by the announcement – everyone that is apart from Grimm and Parquet. I wouldn't go so far as to say that their evident discomfiture actually enhanced my pleasure at the turnaround, but it certainly didn't detract from it. Loathsome as he is, I can at least understand Grimm, he is the enemy after all and he has been comprehensively trounced. Parquet's behaviour just beggars belief however – he works for AFFE, albeit in a squalid and menial capacity, so why isn't he pleased? What's the matter with him?

One final announcement – the politically correct ban on bonuses means pay rises all round. Well, perhaps not all round, we still need to maintain tight control on costs in these economically straitened times so those areas (e.g. compliance) which are not driving the recovery in revenue will need to continue to observe tight budgetary discipline. I must have a word with Bridget; she'll be delighted to pass on the message.

Thurs 26 August: It's a very big week for happy announcements. Today's is that we will shortly be paying back our government loans. Grimm, someone who only two months ago was apoplectic at the prospect of our escape from his clutches is now wreathed with smiles. Doubtless he is already redefining his role as the man who secured AFFE's speedy return to the private sector. The little creep will go far. Sir James Grimm KCMG. I can see it now.

Fri 27 August: An unwanted visit from Parquet (is there any other kind?) He has composed a massive compendium of lessons to be learned from

the crisis which he has modestly chosen to call The Parquet Report. It's almost certainly rubbish but, in any case, I'm certainly not about to read it in order to find out.

Who cares in any case? The crisis is over. I put the report straight in the bin. There's only one lesson worth learning anyway; better a live giant poison squid than a dead lion. It's time to look forward. There's a lot of work to be done to rebuild public confidence in the banking system in general and in AFFE in particular. It's time to return to and to reassert our core values, innovation, yes, but solidity and security too. Time to rebrand the corporation. Time for a new logo – and a new motto. AFFE – Too Big to Fail. I'll put it to the board.

Gershon

~

FIN

The Credit Crunch Diaries

Epilogue

By the autumn of 2009, the financial world had become over-whelmed by a sense of having lived through something terrible – and of having survived it. Stock markets had rallied strongly, borrowing costs had come down and, crucially, bonuses were back. Even house prices in the US and UK had risen for a couple of months. The world economy, after the biggest fall since the 1930s, had stabilised and started to grow again. Unemployment was still rising, however, and most big economies were seeing falling consumer prices – something not seen in a generation. Amidst rebounding optimism the sour and discontented pointed to vast global imbalances and a future crisis in western government finances. It was ever thus.

~